Private Oral Exam Guide

Fifth Edition

The comprehensive
guide to prepare you
for the FAA Oral Exam

by Michael D. Hayes

Aviation Supplies & Academics, Inc.
Newcastle, Washington

Private Oral Exam Guide
Fifth Edition

Aviation Supplies & Academics, Inc.
7005 132nd Place SE
Newcastle, Washington 98059-3153

Printed in the United States of America

00 99 98   9 8 7 6 5 4 3 2 1

ISBN 1-56027-313-5
ASA-OEG-P

Library of Congress Cataloging-in-Publication Data:

Hayes, Michael D.
     Private oral exam guide: the comprehensive guide to prepare
you for the FAA Oral exam / by Michael D. Hayes.
          p.   cm.
     "ASA-OEG-P"—Cover.
     ISBN 1-56027-155-8
     1. Aeronautics—Examinations, questions, etc. 2. Private
flying—Examinations, questions, etc. 3. United States. Federal
Aviation Administration—Examinations—Study guides.
4. Oral examinations. I. Aviation Supplies & Academics, Inc.
II. Title.
TL546.5.H33   1993
629.132'5217'076—dc20   93-12050
                                                    CIP

This guide is dedicated to the many talented students, pilots and flight instructors I have had the opportunity to work with over the years. Also, special thanks to Mark Hayes and many others who supplied the patience, encouragement, and understanding necessary to complete the project.

—M.D.H.

Contents

Continued

5 Cross-Country Flight Planning

6 Night Operations

7 Aeromedical Factors

Introduction

The *Private Oral Exam Guide* is a comprehensive guide designed for student pilots who are involved in training for the Private Pilot Certificate. This guide was originally designed for use in a Part 141 flight school but has quickly become popular with those training under 14 CFR Part 61 who are not affiliated with an approved school. The guide will also prove beneficial to private pilots who wish to refresh their knowledge or who are preparing for a flight review.

The Private Pilot Practical Test Standards book (FAA-S-8081-14S) specifies the areas in which knowledge must be demonstrated by the applicant before issuance of a pilot certificate or rating. The *Private Oral Exam Guide* has been designed to evaluate a pilot's knowledge of those areas. This guide contains questions and answers organized into seven main divisions which represent those areas of knowledge required for the practical test.

During the Private Pilot Oral Exam, an FAA examiner may ask questions pertaining to any of the subject areas within these divisions. Through very intensive post-private pilot checkride de-briefings, we have provided you with the most consistent questions asked along with the information necessary for a knowledgeable response. The guide may be supplemented with other comprehensive study materials as noted in parentheses after each question. For example: (AC 61-21A).

Continued

The abbreviations for these materials and their titles are listed below. Be sure to use the latest revision of these references when reviewing for the test.

14 CFR Part 61	*Certification: Pilots and Flight Instructors*
14 CFR Part 91	*General Operating and Flight Rules*
AC 61-21A	*Flight Training Handbook*
AIM	*Aeronautical Information Manual*
AC 61-23C	*Pilot's Handbook of Aeronautical Knowledge*
AC 00-6A	*Aviation Weather*
AC 00-45D	*Aviation Weather Services*
AC 61-27C	*Instrument Flying Handbook*

All the books listed above are reprinted by ASA and available from aviation retailers nationwide.

A review of the information presented within this guide should provide the necessary preparation for the oral section of an FAA Private Pilot certification or recertification check.

Certificates
and Documents

1

A. Certification

What are the eligibility requirements for a private pilot (airplane) certificate? (14 CFR 61.103)

a. Be at least 17 years of age.

b. Be able to read, speak, write, and understand the English language.

c. Hold at least a current Third-Class Medical Certificate.

d. Pass the FAA Knowledge Exam.

e. Pass an FAA oral and flight test.

B. Privileges and Limitations

1. What privileges and limitations apply to a private pilot? (14 CFR 61.113)

A private pilot may not act as pilot-in-command of an aircraft that is carrying passengers or property for compensation or hire; nor may he/she, for compensation or hire, act as pilot-in-command of an aircraft except in the following cases.

a. In certain business flights if the flight is incidental to employment;

b. A private pilot may not pay less than the pro rata share of the operating expenses of a flight with passengers, provided the expenses involve only fuel, oil, airport costs, or rental fees;

c. An aircraft salesman who has at least 200 hours of logged flight time may demonstrate an aircraft to a prospective buyer;

d. In certain flights for charitable organizations.

2. To act as pilot-in-command or in any other capacity as a required flight crewmember of a civil aircraft, what must a pilot have in his/her personal possession, or readily accessible in the aircraft? (14 CFR 61.3)

a. A current pilot certificate

b. An appropriate current medical certificate

3. What is the definition of a high-performance airplane, and what must you do to act as pilot-in-command of such an airplane? (14 CFR 61.31)

A high-performance airplane is one with an engine of more than 200 horsepower. You must have received ground and flight instruction from an authorized flight instructor who has certified in your logbook that you are competent to act as pilot-in-command of a high-performance airplane.

4. Other than high-performance aircraft, what other types of aircraft (ASEL) now require specific training and logbook endorsements from an appropriately rated flight instructor? (14 CFR 61.31)

High-Altitude Airplanes — No person may act as pilot-in-command of a pressurized airplane that has a service ceiling or maximum operating altitude (whichever is lower), above 25,000 feet MSL unless that person has completed the ground and flight training specified and has received a logbook or training record endorsement from an authorized instructor certifying satisfactory completion of the training.

Tailwheel Airplane — No person may act as pilot-in-command of a tailwheel airplane unless that pilot has received flight instruction from an authorized flight instructor who has found the pilot competent to operate a tailwheel airplane and has made a one-time endorsement so stating in the pilot's logbook. The endorsement is not required if a pilot has logged flight time as pilot-in-command of tailwheel airplanes prior to April 15, 1991.

5. What is the definition of a complex airplane, and what must you do to act as pilot-in-command of such an airplane? (14 CFR 61.31)

A complex airplane is one that has a retractable landing gear, flaps, and a controllable pitch propeller. You must have received and logged ground and flight training from an authorized instructor in a complex airplane, or in a flight simulator or flight training device representative of a complex airplane; you must be found proficient in the operation and systems of the airplane; and you must have received a one-time endorsement in your logbook, from an authorized instructor, who certifies you are proficient to operate a complex airplane.

Note: The training and endorsement required by this regulation is not required if the person has logged flight time as pilot-in-command of a complex airplane, or in a complex airplane flight simulator or training device, prior to August 4, 1997.

C. Currency Requirements

1. What are the requirements to remain current as a private pilot? (14 CFR 61.56, 61.57)

a. Accomplish a flight review (biennial) given in an aircraft for which that pilot is rated by an appropriately rated instructor within the preceding 24 calendar months.

b. To carry passengers, a pilot must have made within the preceding 90 days:

  i. three takeoffs and three landings as the sole manipulator of the flight controls of an aircraft of the same category and class and, if a type rating is required, of the same type.

  ii. if the aircraft is a tailwheel airplane, the landings must have been made to a full stop.

  iii. if operations are to be conducted during the period beginning 1 hour after sunset to 1 hour before sunrise, with passengers on board, the pilot-in-command must have, within the preceding 90 days, made at least three takeoffs and three landings to a full stop during that period in an aircraft of the same category, class, and type (if a type is required) of aircraft to be used.

2. To exercise the privileges of a private pilot certificate, what medical certificate is required, and how long is it valid? (14 CFR 61.23)

You must possess a third-class medical certificate. If the medical certificate was issued before September 16, 1996, it expires at the end of the 24th month after the month of the date of examination shown on the certificate. If it was issued on or after September 16, 1996, it expires at the end of:

a. The 36th month after the month of the date of the examination shown on the certificate if the person has not reached his or her 40th birthday on or before the date of examination; or

b. The 24th month after the month of the date of the examination shown on the certificate if the person has reached his or her 40th birthday on or before the date of the examination.

3. If a pilot changes his/her permanent mailing address and fails to notify the FAA Airmen Certification branch of the new address, how long may the pilot continue to exercise the privileges of his/her pilot certificate? (14 CFR 61.60)

30 days after the date of the move.

D. Aircraft Certificates and Documents

1. What documents are required on board an aircraft prior to flight? (14 CFR 91.203, 91.9)

A irworthiness Certificate
R egistration Certificate
R adio station license*
O wner's manual or operating limitations
W eight and balance data

Note: On Oct. 26th, 1996 the FCC eliminated the individual licensing requirement for all aircraft operating domestically. This means that you do not need a license to operate a two-way VHF radio, radar, or ELT aboard aircraft operating domestically. All other aircraft radio stations must be licensed by the FCC either individually or by fleet. The new rule applies to all aircraft, including scheduled air carriers, air taxis, as well as general aviation aircraft, as long as they fly domestically.

2. How can a pilot determine if his/her aircraft is equipped with a Mode C altitude encoding transponder?

By referencing the current weight and balance equipment list for that aircraft, a pilot could positively determine whether or not a Mode C transponder is installed.

E. Aircraft Maintenance Requirements

1. Who is responsible for ensuring that an aircraft is maintained in an airworthy condition? (14 CFR 91.403)

The owner or operator of an aircraft is primarily responsible for maintaining an aircraft in an airworthy condition.

2. After aircraft inspections have been made and defects have been repaired, who is responsible for determining that the aircraft is in an airworthy condition? (14 CFR 91.7)

The pilot-in-command of a civil aircraft is responsible for determining whether that aircraft is in condition for safe flight. The pilot-in-command shall discontinue the flight when unairworthy mechanical, electrical, or structural conditions occur.

3. What records or documents should be checked to determine that the owner or operator of an aircraft has complied with all required inspections and airworthiness directives? (14 CFR 91.405)

The maintenance records (aircraft and engine logbooks). Each owner or operator of an aircraft shall ensure that maintenance personnel make appropriate entries in the aircraft maintenance records indicating the aircraft has been approved for return to service.

4. What regulations apply concerning the operation of an aircraft that has had alterations or repairs which may have substantially affected its operation in flight? (14 CFR 91.407)

No person may operate or carry passengers in any aircraft that has undergone maintenance, preventative maintenance, rebuilding, or alteration that may have appreciably changed its flight characteristics or substantially affected its operation in flight until an appropriately rated pilot with at least a private pilot certificate

a. flies the aircraft;

b. makes an operational check of the maintenance performed or alteration made; and

c. logs the flight in the aircraft records.

5. How long does the airworthiness certificate of an aircraft remain valid? (14 CFR Part 21)

Standard Airworthiness Certificates are effective as long as the maintenance, preventative maintenance, and alterations are performed in accordance with Parts 43 and 91 and the aircraft is registered in the United States.

6. Can you legally fly an aircraft that has an inoperative flap position indicator?

Unless operations are conducted under 14 CFR 91.213,* the regulations require that all equipment installed on an aircraft in compliance with either the Airworthiness Standards or the Operating Rules must be operative. If equipment originally installed in the aircraft is no longer operative, the Airworthiness Certificate is not valid until such equipment is either repaired or removed from that aircraft.

However, the rules also permit the publication of a Minimum Equipment List (MEL) where compliance with these equipment requirements is not necessary in the interests of safety under all conditions. Deviation from the equipment requirements of the regulation is maintained by alternate means. Experience has shown that with the various levels of redundancy designed into aircraft, operation of every system or component installed may not be necessary when the remaining operative equipment can provide an acceptable level of safety.

See question #8 below.

7. What are "Minimum Equipment Lists"?

A Master Minimum Equipment List (MMEL) is developed by the FAA, with participation by the aviation industry to improve aircraft utilization and thereby provide more convenient and economic air transportation for the public. The FAA-approved MMEL includes only those items of equipment which the Administrator finds may be inoperative and yet maintain an acceptable level of safety by appropriate conditions and limitations.

The MMEL is the basis for development of individual operator MELs which may not be less restrictive than the MMEL and which take into consideration the operator's particular aircraft equipment configuration and operational conditions. The individual operator's MEL, when approved and authorized, permits operation of the aircraft with inoperative equipment.

The MEL is intended to permit operation with inoperative items of equipment for the minimum period of time necessary until repair can be accomplished. It is important that repair be accomplished at the earliest opportunity in order to return the aircraft to its design level of safety and reliability. In order to maintain this level the MMEL establishes limitations on the duration of operation with inoperative equipment.

8. What responsibilities should a pilot be familiar with concerning inoperative equipment on the aircraft? (14 CFR 91.213)

a. No person may take off in an aircraft with inoperative instruments or equipment installed unless:

  i. an approved Minimum Equipment List exists for that aircraft;

  ii. a letter of authorization from the FAA is carried within the aircraft authorizing use of a MEL; and

Continued

      iii. the aircraft records available to the pilot must include an entry describing the inoperable instruments and equipment allowed by the MEL.

  b. A person may take off in an aircraft with inoperative instruments and equipment without an approved Minimum Equipment List provided:

      i. the flight operation is conducted in a non-turbine powered aircraft for which a Master Minimum Equipment List has not been developed; and

      ii. the inoperable instruments and equipment are not part of the VFR-day type certification instruments and equipment prescribed in the applicable airworthiness regulations; and

      iii. the inoperable instruments and equipment are removed from the aircraft, the cockpit control placarded, and the maintenance recorded; or

      iv. the inoperable instruments and equipment are deactivated and placarded "Inoperative"; and

      v. a determination is made by a certificated, appropriately rated pilot or mechanic that the inoperative instruments or equipment do not constitute a hazard to the aircraft.

9. What are the required maintenance inspections for aircraft? (14 CFR 91.409)

No person may operate an aircraft unless, within the preceding 12 calendar months, it has had an annual inspection in accordance with Part 43 and has been approved for return to service. Also, no person may operate an aircraft carrying any person (other than a crewmember) for hire, and no person may give flight instruction for hire in an aircraft which that person provides, unless within the preceding 100 hours of time in service the aircraft has received an annual or 100-hour inspection and has been approved for return to service.

    In summary, if an aircraft is operated for hire (carrying passengers or for flight instruction), it must have a 100-hour inspection as well as an annual inspection when due. If not operated for hire, it must have an annual inspection only.

Note: Be capable of locating the 100-hour and annual inspections in the aircraft and engine logbooks.

10. Under what circumstances can an aircraft be operated if the 100-hour inspection is overdue? (14 CFR 91.409)

The 100-hour limitation may be exceeded by not more than 10 hours while en route to a place where the inspection can be done. The excess time used to reach a place where the inspection can be done must be included in computing the next 100 hours of time in service.

11. What is the difference between an annual inspection and a 100-hour inspection? (14 CFR Part 43)

No differences exist when comparing the content of an annual inspection with that of a 100-hour inspection. The difference is who is allowed to perform these inspections. Only an A&P mechanic with an Inspection Authorization can perform an annual inspection. 100-hour inspections may be performed by any A&P mechanic (no IA required).

12. What are the required equipment inspections for an aircraft? (14 CFR 91.171, 91.207, 91.411, 91.413)

Within the preceding 24 calendar months, the pitot-static system, the transponder, and the altimeter must have been checked, and a record must be kept in the aircraft logbook.

Within the preceding 12 calendar months, the ELT must have been checked, and a record kept in the aircraft logbook.

13. What responsibilities does an owner or operator have concerning maintenance records for their aircraft? (14 CFR 91.417)

Each registered owner or operator shall keep records of the maintenance, preventative maintenance, and alteration and records of the 100-hour, annual, progressive, and other required or approved inspections, as appropriate, for each aircraft (including the airframe) and each engine propeller, rotor and appliance of an aircraft. The records must include:

a. a description (or reference to data acceptable to the Administrator) of the work performed;

Continued

b. the date of completion of the work performed;

c. the signature and certificate number of the person approving the aircraft for return to service; and also

d. a record of the preventative maintenance must be entered in the maintenance records.

14. Define "preventative maintenance." (14 CFR Part 43)

Preventative maintenance items which can be performed by the pilot are listed in Part 43 and include such basic items as oil changes, wheel bearing lubrication, and hydraulic fluid (brakes, landing gear system) refills. However, even if Part 43 permits certain work, do not exceed your personal skill level.

15. What are "Special Flight Permits," and when are they necessary? (14 CFR 91.213, 14 CFR 21.197)

A Special Flight Permit may be issued for an aircraft that may not currently meet applicable airworthiness requirements but is capable of safe flight. These permits are typically issued for the following purposes:

a. Flying an aircraft to a base where repairs, alterations or maintenance are to be performed, or to a point of storage.

b. Delivering or exporting an aircraft.

c. Production flight testing new-production aircraft.

d. Evacuating aircraft from areas of impending danger.

e. Conducting customer demonstration flights in new-production aircraft that have satisfactorily completed production flight tests.

16. How are "Special Flight Permits" obtained?
(14 CFR 21.197)

An applicant for a Special Flight Permit must submit a statement in a form and manner prescribed by the Administrator indicating:

a. Purpose of flight.

b. Proposed itinerary.

c. The crew required to operate the aircraft and its equipment.

d. The ways, if any, in which the aircraft does not comply with applicable airworthiness requirements.

e. Any restriction the applicant considers necessary for safe operation of the aircraft.

f. Any other information considered necessary by the Administrator for the purpose of prescribing operating limitations.

Weather

2

A. Nature of the Atmosphere

1. State the general characteristics in regard to the flow of air around high and low pressure systems in the Northern Hemisphere. (AC 00-6A)

Low Pressure—inward, upward, and counterclockwise

High Pressure—outward, downward, and clockwise

2. What is a "trough"? (AC 00-6A)

A trough (also called a trough line) is an elongated area of relatively low atmospheric pressure. At the surface when air converges into a low, it cannot go outward against the pressure gradient, nor can it go downward into the ground; it must go upward. Therefore, a low or trough is an area of rising air. Rising air is conducive to cloudiness and precipitation; hence the general association of low pressure and bad weather.

3. What is a "ridge"? (AC 00-6A)

A ridge (also called a ridge line) is an elongated area of relatively high atmospheric pressure. Air moving out of a high or ridge depletes the quantity of air; therefore, these are areas of descending air. Descending air favors dissipation of cloudiness; hence the association of high pressure and good weather.

4. What are the standard temperature and pressure values for sea level? (AC 00-6A)

15°C and 29.92" Hg

5. What are "isobars"? (AC 00-6A)

An isobar is a line on a weather chart which connects areas of equal or constant barometric pressure.

6. **If the isobars are relatively close together on a surface weather chart or a constant pressure chart, what information will this provide?** (AC 00-6A)

The spacing of isobars on these charts defines how steep or shallow a pressure gradient is. When isobars are spaced very close together, a steep pressure gradient exists which indicates higher wind speeds. A shallow pressure gradient (isobars not close together) usually means wind speeds will be less.

7. **What causes the winds aloft to flow parallel to the isobars?** (AC 00-6A)

The Coriolis force.

8. **Why do surface winds generally flow across the isobars at an angle?** (AC 00-6A)

Surface friction.

9. **At what rate does atmospheric pressure decrease with an increase in altitude?** (AC 00-6A)

1" Hg per 1,000 feet.

10. **What does "dew point" mean?** (AC 00-6A)

Dew point is the temperature to which a sample of air must be cooled to attain the state of saturation.

11. **When temperature and dew point are close together (within 5°), what type of weather is likely?** (AC 00-6A)

Visible moisture in the form of clouds, dew, or fog. Also, these are ideal conditions for carburetor icing.

12. **What factor primarily determines the type and vertical extent of clouds?** (AC 00-6A)

The stability of the atmosphere.

13. How do you determine the stability of the atmosphere? (AC 00-6A)

By observing the actual lapse rate and comparing it to the standard lapse rate of 3.5°F per 1,000 feet. The "K" index of a stability chart is the primary means of determining stability. In general, stable air cools at a rate less than the standard lapse rate with altitude, and unstable air cools at a rate that is greater than the standard lapse rate.

14. List the effects of stable and unstable air on clouds, turbulence, precipitation and visibility. (AC 00-6A)

	STABLE	UNSTABLE
Clouds	Stratiform	Cumuliform
Turbulence	Smooth	Rough
Precipitation	Steady	Showery
Visibility	Fair to Poor	Good

15. At what altitude above the surface would the pilot expect the bases of cumuliform clouds if the surface temperature is 82° and the dew point is 62°? (AC 00-6A)

You can estimate the height of cumuliform cloud bases using surface temperature/dew point spread. Unsaturated air in a convective current cools at about 5.4°F (3.0°C) per 1,000 feet; dew point decreases at about 1°F (5/9°C). Thus, in a convective current, temperature and dew point converge at about 4.4°F (2.5°C) per 1,000 feet. You can get a quick estimate of a convective cloud base in thousands of feet by rounding the values and dividing into the spread. When using Fahrenheit, divide by 4 and multiply by 1,000. This method of estimating is reliable only with instability, clouds and during the warmer part of the day.

$$\frac{\text{Temperature-dew point}}{4} \times 1{,}000 = \text{Base of clouds}$$

$82 - 62 = 20$

$20 \div 4 = 5$

$5 \times 1{,}000 = 5{,}000$ feet AGL

16. **What will the freezing level be if the field elevation is 1,000 feet and the temperature at the surface is 15°C?** (AC 00-6A)

The freezing level (0°C) can be estimated by subtracting 2°C per 1,000 feet (average lapse rate) from 15°. For this example the freezing level will be at 8,500 MSL.

17. **What conditions are necessary for structural icing to occur?** (AC 00-6A)

Visible moisture and below freezing temperatures at the point moisture strikes the aircraft.

18. **What are the two main types of icing?** (AC 00-6A)

Structural and induction.

19. **Name four types of structural ice.** (AC 00-6A)

Clear ice—forms when large drops strike the aircraft surface and slowly freeze.

Rime ice—small drops strike the aircraft and freeze rapidly.

Mixed ice—combination of above; supercooled water drops varying in size.

Frost—ice crystal deposits formed by sublimation when temperature and dew point are below freezing.

20. **What action is recommended if you inadvertently encounter icing conditions?** (AC 00-6A)

Change course and/or altitude; usually, climb to a higher altitude, if possible.

21. Is frost considered to be hazardous to flight? Why? (AC 00-6A)

Yes, because while frost does not change the basic aerodynamic shape of the wing, the roughness of its surface spoils the smooth flow of air, thus causing a slowing of airflow. This slowing of the air causes early airflow separation, resulting in a loss of lift. Even a small amount of frost on airfoils may prevent an aircraft from becoming airborne at normal takeoff speed. It is also possible that, once airborne, an aircraft could have insufficient margin of airspeed above stall so that moderate gusts or turning flight could produce incipient or complete stalling.

22. What factors must be present for a thunderstorm to form? (AC 00-6A)

a. A source of lift (heating, fast-moving front)

b. Unstable air (nonstandard lapse rate)

c. High moisture content (temperature/dew point close)

23. What are the three stages of a thunderstorm? (AC 00-6A)

Cumulus stage—Updrafts cause raindrops to increase in size.

Mature stage—Rain at earth's surface; it falls through or immediately beside the updrafts; lightning; perhaps roll clouds.

Dissipating stage—Downdrafts and rain begin to dissipate.

24. What is a "temperature inversion"? (AC 00-6A)

An inversion is an increase in temperature with height—a reversal of the normal decrease with height. An inversion aloft permits warm rain to fall through cold air below. Temperature in the cold air can be critical to icing. A ground-based inversion favors poor visibility by trapping fog, smoke, and other restrictions into low levels of the atmosphere. The air is stable, with little or no turbulence.

25. State two basic ways that fog may form. (AC 00-6A)

a. Cool air to the dew point

b. Adding moisture to the air

26. Name several types of fog. (AC 00-6A)

a. Radiation fog

b. Advection fog

c. Upslope fog

d. Steam fog

e. Precipitation-induced fog

27. What causes radiation fog to form? (AC 00-6A)

The ground cools the adjacent air to the dew point on calm, clear nights.

28. What is advection fog and where is it most likely to form? (AC 00-6A)

Advection fog results from the transport of warm humid air over a cold surface. A pilot can expect advection fog to form primarily along coastal areas during the winter. Unlike radiation fog, it may occur with winds, cloudy skies, over a wide geographic area, and at any time of the day or night.

29. Why is fog a major operational concern to pilots? (AC 00-6A)

It is of primary concern during takeoffs and landings. Fog can reduce vertical and horizontal visibilities to zero-zero. It can occur instantly from a clear condition, making takeoffs, landings, and even taxiing, potentially hazardous operations.

30. Define the term "wind shear," and state the areas in which it is likely to occur. (AC 00-6A)

Wind shear is defined as the rate of change of wind velocity (direction and/or speed) per unit distance; conventionally expressed as vertical or horizontal wind shear. It may occur at any level in the atmosphere but three areas are of special concern:

a. Wind shear with a low-level temperature inversion.

b. Wind shear in a frontal zone or thunderstorm.

c. Clear air turbulence (CAT) at high levels associated with a jet stream or strong circulation.

31. Why is wind shear an operational concern to pilots? (AC 00-6A)

Wind shear is an operational concern because unexpected changes in wind speed and direction can be potentially very hazardous to aircraft operations at low altitudes on approach to and departing from airports.

B. Obtaining Weather Information

1. What is the primary means of obtaining a weather briefing? (AIM 7-1-2)

The primary source is an individual briefing obtained from a briefer at the AFSS/FSS. These briefings, which are tailored to your specific flight, are available 24 hours a day through the use of the toll-free number (1-800-WX BRIEF).

2. What are some examples of other sources of weather information? (AIM 7-1-2)

a. Telephone Information Briefing Service (TIBS) (AFSS)

b. Transcribed Weather Broadcasts (TWEB)

c. Telephone Access to TWEB (TEL-TWEB)

d. Weather and aeronautical information from numerous private industry sources

e. The Direct User Access System (DUATS)

3. Where can you find a listing of FSS and weather information numbers? (AIM 7-1-2)

Numbers for these services can be found in the Airport/Facility Directory under the "FAA and NWS Telephone Numbers" section. They are also listed in the U.S. Government section of the local telephone directory.

4. What types of weather briefings are available from an FSS briefer? (AIM 7-1-3)

Standard Briefing—Request when you are planning a flight and you have not received a previous briefing or have not received preliminary information through mass dissemination media (TWEB, PATWAS, DUAT, etc.).

Abbreviated Briefing—Request when you need information to supplement mass disseminated data, update a previous briefing, or when you need only one or two items.

Outlook Briefing—Request whenever your proposed time of departure is six or more hours from the time of the briefing; for planning purposes only.

Inflight Briefing—Request when needed to update a preflight briefing.

5. What pertinent information should a weather briefing include? (AIM 7-1-3)

a. Adverse Conditions

b. VFR Flight Not Recommended

c. Synopsis

d. Current Conditions

e. Enroute Forecast

f. Destination Forecast

g. Winds Aloft

h. Notices to Airmen (NOTAMs)

i. ATC Delay

j. Pilots may obtain the following from AFSS/FSS briefers upon request: Information on MTRs and MOAs, a review of printed NOTAM publications, approximate density altitude information, information on air traffic services and rules, customs/immigration procedures, ADIZ rules, search and rescue, LORAN, NOTAM, GPS RAIM availability, and other assistance as required.

6. What is EFAS? (AIM 7-1-4)

Enroute Flight Advisory Service (EFAS) is specifically designed to provide enroute aircraft with timely and meaningful weather advisories pertinent to the type of flight intended, route of flight, and altitude. In conjunction with this service, EFAS is also a central collection and distribution point for pilot-reported weather information (PIREPS). EFAS provides communications capabilities for aircraft flying at 5,000 feet above ground level to 17,500 feet MSL on a common frequency of 122.0 MHz. It is also known as "Flight Watch." Discrete EFAS frequencies have been established to ensure communications coverage from 18,000 through 45,000 feet MSL serving in each specific ARTCC area. These discrete frequencies may be used below 18,000 feet when coverage permits reliable communication.

7. What is HIWAS? (AIM 7-1-9)

Hazardous In-flight Weather Advisory Service (HIWAS) is a continuous broadcast of in-flight weather advisories including summarized Aviation Weather Warnings, SIGMETs, Convective SIGMETs, Center Weather Advisories, AIRMETs, and urgent PIREPs. HIWAS is an additional source of hazardous weather information which makes this data available on a continuous basis.

C. Aviation Weather Reports and Observations

1. What is a METAR? (AC 00-45D)

METAR, or Aviation Routine Weather Report: An hourly surface observation of conditions observed at an airport. A new international weather reporting code now being used by all countries of the world.

2. Describe the basic elements of a METAR. (AC 00-45D)

A METAR contains the following sequence of elements:

a. Two types of reports — METAR (routine observation) and SPECI (special observation)

b. Station designator — ICAO four-letter identifier

c. Time of report — four-digit time group appended with "Z" to denote Coordinated Universal Time

d. Wind — Five-digit group: first three digits, direction of the wind from; next two digits, the speed in knots

e. Visibility — reported in statute miles

f. Weather and obstructions to visibility — reported in the format: INTENSITY/PROXIMITY/DESCRIPTOR/PRECIPITATION/ OBSTRUCTION TO VISIBILITY/OTHER

g. Sky conditions — reported in the format: AMOUNT/HEIGHT/ TYPE or VERTICAL VISIBILITY

h. Temperature and dew point — reported in two-digit form in degrees centigrade

i. Altimeter setting — reported in four-digit form in inches of mercury

j. Remarks — operationally significant weather, beginning and ending times of certain weather phenomena and low-level wind shear

Example: METAR KBNA 1250Z 33018KT 290V360 1/2SM
          R31/2700FT +SN BLSNFG VV00800/M03 A2991
          RMK RERAE42SNB42

3. **Describe several types of Automated Surface Observations now available.** (AC 00-45D)

   ASOS — Automated Surface Observation System is becoming the primary surface weather observing system of the United States. Installation and operation is a joint effort of the NWS, the FAA and the Department of Defense. ASOS provides continuous minute-by-minute observations and performs the basic functions necessary to generate a Surface Aviation Observation and other weather information. When fully implemented, ASOS will more than double the number of full-time surface weather observing locations (between 900 and 1,700 locations).

   AWOS — Automated Weather Observation System, installed by the FAA at selected airports around the country. This system consists of automated reports of ceiling/sky conditions, visibility, temperature, dew point, wind direction/speeds/gusts, altimeter setting, and if certain conditions are met, automated remarks containing density altitude, variable visibility and variable wind direction. Automated observations are broadcast on ground-to-air radio and made available on a telephone answering device.

   AMOS — Automatic Meteorological Observing Station is a solid state system capable of automatically observing temperature, dew point, wind direction and speed, pressure (altimeter setting), peak wind speed, and precipitation accumulation. The field sensors are tied directly to the FAA observation network. It transmits a weather report whenever the station is polled by the circuits.

4. **What are PIREPs (UA), and where are they usually found?** (AC 00-45D)

   An abbreviation for "Pilot Reports," they contain information concerning weather as observed by pilots en route. Required elements for all PIREPs are message type, location, time, flight level, type of aircraft, and at least one weather element encountered. All altitudes are MSL unless otherwise noted. Distances are in nautical miles, and time is in UTC. A PIREP is usually transmitted as an individual report but can be appended to a surface aviation weather report or placed into collectives.

5. What are Radar Weather Reports (SD)? (AC 00-45D)

Thunderstorms and general areas of precipitation can be observed by radar. Most radar stations report each hour at H+35 with intervening special reports as required. The report includes the type, intensity, intensity trend, and location of the precipitation. Also included is the echo top of the precipitation and if significant, the base echo. All heights are reported above Mean Sea Level (MSL). Radar Weather Reports help pilots to plan ahead to avoid thunderstorm areas. Once airborne, however, they must depend on visual sighting or airborne radar to evade individual storms.

D. Aviation Weather Forecasts

1. What are Terminal Aerodrome Forecasts (TAFs)? (AC 00-45D)

A TAF is a concise statement of the expected meteorological conditions at an airport during a specified period (usually 24 hours). TAFs are issued in the following format:

a. Two types: routine and amended forecast issuance

b. Location: ICAO four-letter location identifiers

c. Issuance time: six-digit group giving date (first two digits) and time (last four digits) in UTC

d. Valid time: four-digit group giving valid time (usually 24 hours); amended forecasts may be less than 24 hours

e. Forecast: basic format is WIND/VISIBILITY/WEATHER/ SKY CONDITION

2. What is an Aviation Area Forecast (FA)? (AC 00-45D)

An Aviation Area Forecast (FA) is a forecast of general weather conditions over an area the size of several states. It is used to determine forecast enroute weather and to interpolate conditions at airports which do not have TAFs issued. FAs are issued three times a day for each of the contiguous 48 states.

3. What information is provided by an Aviation Area Forecast (FA)? (AC 00-45D)

The FA is comprised of four sections:

a. Communications and product header section — identifies the office from which the FA is issued, the date and time of issue, the product name, the valid times and the states and/or areas covered by the FA.

b. Precautionary statement section — between the communications/products headers and the body of the forecast are three precautionary statements which are in all Area Forecasts:

SEE AIRMET SIERRA FOR IFR CONDITIONS AND MTN OBSC

This alerts user that IFR conditions and/or mountain obscurement may be occurring or may be forecast to occur in a portion of the FA area.

TSTMS IMPLY PSBL SVR OR GTR TURBC SVR ICG LLWS AND IFR CONDS

A reminder of the hazards existing in all thunderstorms.

NON MSL HGTS ARE DENOTED BY AGL OR CIG

This alerts user that heights, for the most part, are heights above sea level. All heights are in hundreds of feet. The tops of clouds, turbulence, icing and freezing level heights are always MSL. Heights above ground level are noted in either of the following ways: ceilings by definition are above ground; therefore, the contraction "CIG" indicates above ground. The contraction "AGL" means above ground level; thus, if the contraction "AGL" or "CIG" is not denoted, height is automatically above MSL.

c. Synopsis section — a brief summary of the location and movements of fronts, pressure systems, and circulation patterns for an 18-hour period. References to low ceilings and/or visibilities, strong winds, or any other phenomena the forecaster considers useful, may also be included.

Continued

d. VFR Clouds and Weather section — contains a 12-hour specific forecast, followed by a six-hour (18-hour in Alaska) categorical outlook giving a total forecast period of 18 hours (30 hours in Alaska). The VFR CLDS/WX section is usually several paragraphs long. The breakdown may be by states or by well-known geographical areas. The specific forecast section gives a general description of clouds and weather which cover an area greater than 3,000 square miles and is significant to VFR flight operations.

4. What are In-flight Aviation Weather Advisories (WST, WS, WA)? (AC 00-45D)

In-flight Aviation Weather Advisories are forecasts that advise enroute aircraft of development of potentially hazardous weather. All heights are referenced to MSL, except in the case of ceilings (CIG) which indicates above ground level. There are three types: Convective SIGMET (WST), SIGMET (WS) and AIRMET (WA).

5. What is a Convective SIGMET? (AC 00-45D)

Convective SIGMETs (WST) implies severe or greater turbulence, severe icing and low-level wind shear. They may be issued for any convective situation which the forecaster feels is hazardous to all categories of aircraft. Convective SIGMET bulletins are issued for the Eastern (E), Central (C) and Western (W) United States (Convective SIGMETs are not issued for Alaska or Hawaii). Bulletins are issued hourly at H+55. Special bulletins are issued at any time as required and updated at H+55. The text of the bulletin consists of either an observation and a forecast, or just a forecast. The forecast is valid for up to 2 hours.

a. Severe thunderstorm due to:

  i. Surface winds greater than or equal to 50 knots.

  ii. Hail at the surface greater than or equal to 3/4 inches in diameter.

  iii. Tornadoes

b. Embedded thunderstorms

c. A line of thunderstorms

d. Thunderstorms greater than or equal to VIP level 4 affecting 40 percent or more of an area at least 3,000 square miles.

6. What is a SIGMET (WS)? (AC 00-45D)

A SIGMET (WS) advises of non-convective weather that is potentially hazardous to all aircraft. SIGMETs are issued for the six areas corresponding to the FA areas. The maximum forecast period is four hours. In the conterminous U.S., SIGMETs are issued when the following phenomena occur or are expected to occur:

a. Severe icing not associated with a thunderstorm;

b. Severe or extreme turbulence or clear air turbulence (CAT) not associated with thunderstorms;

c. Duststorms, sandstorms or volcanic ash lowering surface or in-flight visibilities to below 3 miles;

d. Volcanic eruption.

7. What is an AIRMET (WA)? (AC 00-45D)

AIRMETs (WA) are advisories of significant weather phenomena but describe conditions at intensities lower than those which trigger SIGMETs. AIRMETS are intended for dissemination to all pilots in the preflight and enroute phase of flight to enhance safety. AIRMET bulletins are issued on a scheduled basis every 6 hours and contain details on one or more of the following phenomena when they occur or are forecast to occur:

a. Moderate icing;

b. Moderate turbulence;

c. Sustained surface winds of 30 knots or more;

d. Ceilings less than 1,000 feet and/or visibilities less than 3 miles affecting over 50 percent of the area at one time;

e. Extensive mountain obscuration.

8. What is a TWEB? (AC 00-45D)

The Transcribed Weather Enroute Broadcasts (TWEBs) are similar to area forecasts, except that more specific information is provided in a route format. They provide forecast sky cover height and amount of cloud bases, cloud tops, visibility (including vertical visibility), weather, and obstructions to vision are described for a corridor 25 miles on either side of the route. Cloud bases and tops are always MSL unless noted. Ceilings are always above ground level (AGL). TWEBs are issued by the WSFOs three times a day according to time zone. The TWEB forecast is valid for a 15-hour period.

9. What is a Winds and Temperatures Aloft Forecast (FD)? (AC 00-45D)

Winds and temperatures aloft are forecast for specific locations in the contiguous U.S. and also for a network of locations in Alaska and Hawaii. Forecasts are made twice daily based on 00Z and 12Z data for use during specific time intervals. FDs contain the following characteristics:

a. A four-digit group will show wind direction, in reference to true north, and wind speed in knots.

b. A six-digit group will include forecast temperatures in degrees Celsius.

c. Since temperatures above 24,000 feet are always negative, the minus sign is omitted.

d. Through 12,000 feet the levels are true altitude, and above 18,000 feet the levels are pressure altitude.

e. No winds are forecast within 1,500 feet of station elevation.

f. No temperatures are forecast for the 3,000-foot level or for any level within 2,500 feet of station elevation.

g. If the coded direction is more than "36," then the wind speed is 100 knots or more.

h. If the wind speed is forecast to be 200 knots or greater, the wind group is coded as 199 knots.

i. When the forecast speed is less than 5 knots, the coded group is "9900" and reads "light and variable."

10. What valuable information can be determined from Winds and Temperatures Aloft Forecasts (FD)? (AC 00-45D)

Most favorable altitude—based on winds and direction of flight.

Areas of possible icing—by noting air temperatures of +2°C to -20°C.

Temperature inversions.

Turbulence—by observing abrupt changes in wind direction and speed at different altitudes.

11. What are Center Weather Advisories (CWA)? (AC 00-45D)

A Center Advisory (CWA) is an unscheduled in-flight air crew, flow control, air traffic advisory for use in anticipating and avoiding adverse weather conditions in the en route and terminal areas. The CWA is not a flight planning forecast, but a forecast for conditions beginning within the next two hours. Maximum valid time for a CWA is two hours.

12. What is a Convective Outlook (AC)? (AC 00-45D)

A Convective Outlook (AC) describes the prospects for general thunderstorm activity during the following 24 hours. Areas in which there is high, moderate, or slight risk of severe thunderstorms are included as well as areas where thunderstorms may approach severe limits. Outlooks are transmitted at 0700Z and 1500Z and are valid until 1200Z the next day.

E. Aviation Weather Charts

1. Give some examples of current weather charts available at the FSS or NWSO used in flight planning. (AC 00-45D)

a. Surface Analysis Chart

b. Weather Depiction Chart

c. Radar Summary Chart

d. Significant Weather Prognostic Chart

Continued

e. Winds and Temperatures Aloft Chart

f. Composite Moisture Stability Chart

g. Severe Weather Outlook Chart

h. Constant Pressure Analysis Chart

i. Tropopause Data Chart

j. Volcanic Ash Forecast Transport and Dispersion Chart

2. What is a Surface Analysis Chart? (AC 00-45D)

This is a computer-prepared chart that covers the contiguous 48 states and adjacent areas. The chart is transmitted every three hours. The surface analysis chart provides a ready means of locating pressure systems and fronts. It also gives an overview of winds, temperatures and dew point temperatures at chart time. When using the chart, keep in mind that weather moves and conditions change. Using the surface analysis chart in conjunction with other information gives a more complete weather picture.

3. What information does a Weather Depiction Chart provide? (AC 00-45D)

The weather depiction chart is computer-prepared from Surface Aviation Observations. This chart gives a broad overview of the observed flying category conditions at the valid time of the chart. The chart begins at 01Z each day, is transmitted at three-hour intervals, and is valid at the time of the plotted data. The plotted data for each station area are: total sky cover, cloud height or ceiling, weather and obstructions to vision and visibilities. The weather depiction chart is an ideal place to begin in preparing for a weather briefing and flight planning. From this chart one can get a "birds eye" view of areas of favorable and adverse weather conditions at chart time.

4. Define the terms: IFR, MVFR and VFR. (AC 00-45D)

IFR: Ceilings less than 1,000 and/or visibilities less than 3 miles (Instrument Flight Rules)

MVFR: (Marginal VFR) Ceiling 1,000 to 3,000 feet inclusive and/or visibility 3 to 5 miles inclusive

VFR: No ceiling, or ceiling greater than 3,000 and visibility greater than 5 miles (Visual Flight Rules)

5. What are Radar Summary Charts? (AC 00-45D)

A radar summary chart graphically displays a collection of radar weather reports (SDs). This computer-generated chart is constructed from regularly scheduled radar observations and is valid at the time of the reports (H+35), i.e. 35 minutes past each hour. These charts are available between 16 and 24 hours daily, depending on the system being used. The chart displays the type of precipitation echoes, their intensity, intensity trend, configuration, coverage, echo tops and bases, and movement. Severe weather watches are plotted if they are in effect when the chart is valid. The radar summary chart aids in preflight planning by identifying general areas and movement of precipitation and/or thunderstorms. Anything shown on this chart along or near a pilot's route of flight must be taken into consideration and noted carefully.

Note: Radar detects only drops or ice particles of precipitation size, it does not detect clouds and fog. Therefore, the absence of echoes does not guarantee clear weather, and cloud tops may be higher than the tops detected by radar. The chart must be used in conjunction with other charts, reports, and forecasts.

6. What are Significant Weather Prognostic Charts? (AC 00-45D)

Significant weather prognostic charts, called "progs," portray forecast weather which may influence flight planning. Significant weather progs are both manually and computer-prepared for the conterminous U.S. and adjacent areas. The U.S. low-level

Continued

significant weather prog is designed for domestic flight planning to 24,000 feet MSL and a U.S. high-level prog is for domestic flights from 24,000 feet to 63,000 feet MSL. Chart legends include valid time in UTC.

7. Describe a U.S. Low-Level Significant Weather Prog Chart. (AC 00-45D)

The low-level prog is a four-panel chart. The two lower panels are 12- and 24-hour surface progs. The two upper panels are 12- and 24-hour progs of significant weather from the surface to 400 millibars (24,000 feet MSL). The charts show conditions as they are forecast to be at the valid time of the chart. This chart is issued four times daily with the 12- and 24-hour forecasts based on the 00Z, 06Z, 12Z and 18Z synoptic data. The two surface prog panels depict fronts, significant troughs and pressure centers, and also outline areas of forecast precipitation and/or thunderstorms. The two upper panels depict IFR, MVFR, turbulence, and freezing levels.

8. What is a Forecast Winds and Temperatures Aloft Chart (FD)? (AC 00-45D)

This chart is a computer-generated chart depicting both observed and forecast winds and temperatures aloft. Forecast winds and temperatures aloft are prepared for eight levels on eight separate panels. The levels are 6,000, 9,000, 12,000, 18,000, 24,000, 30,000, 34,000 and 39,000 feet MSL. They are available daily as 12 hour progs valid at 1200Z and 0000Z. These charts are typically used to determine winds at a proposed altitude or to select the best altitude for a proposed flight. Temperatures also can be determined from the forecast charts. Interpolation must be used to determine winds and temperatures at a level between charts and data when the time period is other than the valid time of the chart.

9. What is a Composite Moisture Stability Chart? (AC 00-45D)

This is an analysis chart using observed upper air data. The chart is composed of four panels including stability, freezing level, precipitable water and, average relative humidity. This computer-generated chart is available twice daily with valid times of 12Z and 00Z. It is used to determine the characteristics of a particular weather system in terms of stability, moisture, and possible aviation hazards. Even though this chart is several hours old when received, these characteristics will tend to move with the weather system. Exercise caution, as modification of these characteristics could occur through development, dissipation, or the movement of the system.

10. What is a Severe Weather Outlook Chart? (AC 00-45D)

The Severe Weather Outlook Chart is a 48-hour outlook for thunderstorm activity. The chart is presented in two panels. The left-hand panel covers the first 24-hour period beginning at 12Z and depicts areas of possible general thunderstorm activity as well as severe thunderstorms. The right-hand panel covers the following day beginning at 12Z and is an outlook for the possibility of severe thunderstorms only. This computer-prepared chart is issued once daily in the morning (about 08Z). This chart is strictly for advanced planning. It alerts all interests to the possibility of future thunderstorm development.

11. What are Constant Pressure Analysis Charts? (AC 00-45D)

Any surface of equal pressure in the atmosphere is a constant pressure surface. A constant pressure analysis chart is an upper air weather map where all information depicted is at the specified pressure of the chart. From these charts, a pilot can approximate the observed air temperature, wind, and temperature-dew point spread along a proposed route. They also depict highs, lows, troughs, and ridges aloft by the height contour patterns resembling isobars on a surface map. Twice daily, six computer-prepared constant pressure charts are transmitted by facsimile for six pressure levels:

850 mb .... 5,000 ft
700 mb .... 10,000 ft
500 mb .... 18,000 ft
300 mb .... 30,000 ft
250 mb .... 34,000 ft
200 mb .... 39,000 ft

12. Describe a Volcanic Ash Forecast Transport and Dispersion Chart. (AC 00-45D)

This VAFTAD chart presents the relative concentrations of ash following a volcanic eruption for three layers of the atmosphere in addition to a composite of ash concentration through the atmosphere. The chart focuses on hazards to aircraft flight operations caused by volcanic eruption with an emphasis on the ash cloud location in time and space. It uses National Meteorological Center forecast data to determine the location of ash concentrations over 6-hour and 12-hour time intervals. The chart is strictly for advanced flight planning purposes. It is not intended to take the place of SIGMETs regarding volcanic eruptions and ash.

Determining Performance and Limitations

3

A. Aerodynamics

1. What are the four dynamic forces that act on an airplane? (AC 61-21A)

The airplane in straight-and-level unaccelerated flight is acted on by four forces:

Lift—the upward acting force

Weight—or gravity, the downward acting force

Thrust—the forward acting force

Drag—the backward acting force

2. What flight condition will result in the four forces being equal? (AC 61-21A)

In steady-state, unaccelerated flight, lift equals weight, and thrust equals drag. Any inequality between lift and weight will result in a change in the rate of climb or descent. Any inequality between thrust and drag while maintaining steady-state flight will result in a change in the rate of climb or descent.

3. What is an airfoil? State some examples. (AC 61-21A)

An airfoil is a device which gets a useful reaction from air moving over its surface, namely LIFT. Wings, horizontal tail surfaces, vertical tail surfaces, and propellers are examples of airfoils.

4. What is the "angle of incidence"? (AC 61-21A)

The angle of incidence is the angle formed by the longitudinal axis of the airplane and the chord of the wing. It is measured by the angle at which the wing is attached to the fuselage. The angle of incidence is fixed and cannot be changed by the pilot.

5. What is a "relative wind"? (AC 61-21A)

The relative wind is the direction of the airflow with respect to the wing. When a wing is moving forward and downward the relative wind moves backward and upward. The flight path and relative wind are always parallel but travel in opposite directions.

6. What is the "angle of attack"? (AC 61-21A)

The angle of attack is the angle between the wing chord line and the direction of the relative wind; it can be changed by the pilot.

7. What is "Bernoulli's Principle"? (AC 61-21A)

Bernoulli's Principle—The pressure of a fluid (liquid or gas) decreases at points where the speed of the fluid increases. In the case of airflow, high speed flow is associated with low pressure and low speed flow with high pressure. The airfoil of an aircraft is designed to increase the velocity of the airflow above its surface, thereby decreasing pressure above the airfoil. Simultaneously, the impact of the air on the lower surface of the airfoil increases the pressure below. This combination of pressure decrease above and increase below produces lift.

8. What are several factors which will affect both lift and drag? (AC 61-23C)

Wing area—Lift and drag acting on a wing are roughly proportional to the wing area. A pilot can change wing area by using certain types of flaps (i.e., Fowler flaps).

Shape of the airfoil—As the upper curvature of an airfoil is increased (up to a certain point) the lift produced increases. Lowering an aileron or flap device can accomplish this. Also, ice or frost on a wing can disturb normal airflow, changing its camber, and disrupting its lifting capability.

Angle of attack—As angle of attack is increased, both lift and drag are increased, up to a certain point.

Velocity of the air—An increase in velocity of air passing over the wing increases lift and drag.

Air density—Lift and drag vary directly with the density of the air. As air density increases, lift and drag increase. As air density decreases, lift and drag decrease. Air density is affected by these factors: pressure, temperature, and humidity.

9. What is "torque effect"? (AC 61-21A)

Torque effect is the force which causes the airplane to have a tendency to swerve (yaw) to the left, and is created by the engine and propeller. It is greatest when at low airspeeds with high power settings and a high angle of attack.

10. What are the four factors that contribute to torque effect? (AC 61-21A)

Torque reaction of the engine and propeller. For every action there is an equal and opposite reaction. The rotation of the propeller (from the cockpit) to the right, tends to roll or bank the airplane to the left.

Gyroscopic effect of the propeller. Gyroscopic precession applies here: the resultant action or deflection of a spinning object when a force is applied to the outer rim of its rotational mass. If the axis of a propeller is tilted, the resulting force will be exerted 90° ahead in the direction of rotation and in the same direction as the applied force. It is most noticeable on takeoffs in taildraggers when the tail is raised.

Remember: Nose yaws to the right when nose is moving upward. Nose yaws to the left when nose is moving downward.

Corkscrewing effect of the propeller slipstream. High-speed rotation of an airplane propeller results in a corkscrewing rotation to the slipstream as it moves rearward. At high propeller speeds and low forward speeds (as in a takeoff), the slipstream strikes the vertical tail surface on the left side pushing the tail to the right and yawing the airplane to the left.

Asymmetrical loading of the propeller (P-Factor). When an airplane is flying with a high angle of attack, the bite of the downward moving propeller blade is greater than the bite of the upward moving blade. This is due to the downward moving blade meeting the oncoming relative wind at a greater angle of attack than the upward moving blade. Consequently there is greater thrust on the downward moving blade on the right side, and this forces the airplane to yaw to the left.

11. What other factor (besides the corkscrew effect of the propeller slipstream) contributes to the tendency of a tricycle gear airplane to swerve to the left on takeoff (prior to rotation)? (AC 61-21A)

As power is applied, torque effect will cause an airplane to roll left which creates an increased downward force on the left main gear tire. As a result, more friction is created on the left tire resulting in a tendency of the airplane to yaw or swerve to the left.

12. What is "centrifugal force"? (AC 61-21A)

Centrifugal force frequently acts on an airplane in turning flight. It is the reaction of the airplane to a change in the direction of flight and acts opposite to the horizontal component of lift.

13. What is "load factor"? (AC 61-21A)

Load factor is the ratio of the total airload acting on the airplane to the gross weight of the airplane. Any force applied to an airplane to deflect its flight from a straight line produces a stress on its structure; the amount of this force is termed "load factor." For example, a load factor of 3 Gs means that the total load on an airplane's structure is 3 times its gross weight.

14. For what two reasons is load factor important to pilots? (AC 61-21A)

a. Because of the obviously dangerous overload that it is possible for a pilot to impose on the aircraft structure.

b. Because an increased load factor increases the stalling speed and makes stalls possible at seemingly safe flight speeds.

15. What situations may result in load factors reaching the maximum or being exceeded? (AC 61-21A)

Level Turns—The load factor increases at a terrific rate after a bank has reached 45° or 50°. The load factor in a 60°-bank turn is 2 Gs. The load factor in a 80°-bank turn is 5.76 Gs. The wing must produce lift equal to these load factors if altitude is to be maintained.

Turbulence—Severe vertical gusts cause a sudden increase in angle of attack, resulting in large loads which are resisted by the inertia of the airplane.

Speed—The amount of excess load that can be imposed upon the wing depends on how fast the airplane is flying. At speeds below maneuvering speed, the airplane will stall before the load factor can become excessive. At speeds above maneuvering speed, the limit load factor for which an airplane is stressed can be exceeded by abrupt or excessive application of the controls or by strong turbulence.

16. What are the different operational categories for aircraft and within which category does your aircraft fall? (AC 61-21A)

The maximum safe load factors (limit load factors) specified for airplanes in the various categories are as follows:

a. Normal .... +3.8 to -1.52

b. Utility (mild aerobatics including spins) .... +4.4 to -1.76

c. Aerobatic .... +6.0 to -3.00

17. What effect does an increase in load factor have on stalling speed? (AC 61-21A)

As load factor increases, stalling speed increases. Load factor increases when an airplane follows a curved flight path, turns, pulls out from a dive, or a sudden or excessive application of back pressure is applied on the control wheel. Consequently, the stalling speed will also increase.

18. Define the term "maneuvering speed." (AC 61-21A)

Maneuvering speed is the maximum speed at which abrupt control movement can be applied or at which the airplane could be flown in turbulence without exceeding design load factor limits.

19. Discuss the effect on maneuvering speed of an increase or decrease in weight. (AC 61-21A)

Maneuvering speed increases with an increase in weight and decreases with a decrease in weight. An aircraft operating at a reduced weight is more vulnerable to rapid accelerations encountered during flight through turbulence or gusts. Design limit load factors could be exceeded if a reduction in maneuvering speed is not accomplished. An aircraft operating at or near gross weight in turbulent air is much less likely to exceed design limit load factors and may be operated at the published maneuvering speed for gross weight if necessary.

20. What causes an airplane to stall? (AC 61-21A)

An airplane stalls when the critical angle of attack has been exceeded. When the angle of attack increases to approximately 18° to 20°, the air can no longer flow smoothly over the top wing surface. Because the airflow cannot make such a great change in direction so quickly, it becomes impossible for the air to follow the contour of the wing. This is the stalling or critical angle of attack. This can occur at any airspeed, in any attitude, with any power setting.

21. What is a "spin"? (AC 61-67B)

A spin may be described as a controlled or uncontrolled maneuver in which the aircraft descends in a helical path while flying at an angle of attack greater than the angle of maximum lift. Spins result from aggravated stalls in either a slip or a skid. If a stall does not occur, a spin cannot occur. In a stall, one wing will often drop before the other, and the nose will yaw in the direction of the low wing.

22. What causes a spin? (AC 61-67B)

The primary cause of an inadvertent spin is exceeding the critical angle of attack for a given stall speed while executing a turn with excessive or insufficient rudder and, to a lesser extent, aileron.

23. When are spins most likely to occur? (AC 61-67B)

A stall/spin situation can occur in any phase of flight but is most likely to occur in the following situations:

a. Engine failure on takeoff during climbout—pilot tries to stretch glide to landing area by increasing back pressure or makes an uncoordinated turn back to departure runway at a relatively low airspeed.

b. Crossed-control turn from base to final (slipping or skidding turn)—pilot overshoots final (possibly due to a crosswind) and makes uncoordinated turn at a low airspeed.

c. Engine failure on approach to landing—pilot tries to stretch glide to runway by increasing back pressure.

d. Go-around with full nose-up trim—pilot applies power with full flaps and nose-up trim combined with uncoordinated use of rudder.

e. Go-around with improper flap retraction—pilot applies power and retracts flaps rapidly resulting in a rapid sink rate followed by an instinctive increase in back pressure.

24. What procedure should be used to recover from an inadvertent spin? (AC 61-67B)

a. Close the throttle (if not already accomplished).

b. Neutralize the ailerons.

c. Apply full opposite rudder.

d. Briskly move the elevator control forward to approximately the neutral position. (Some aircraft require merely a relaxation of back pressure; others require full forward elevator pressure).

e. Once the stall is broken the spinning will stop. Neutralize the rudder when the spinning stops.

f. When the rudder is neutralized, gradually apply enough aft elevator pressure to return to level flight.

25. What causes "adverse yaw"? (AC 61-21A)

When turning an airplane to the left for example, the downward deflected aileron on the right produces more lift on the right wing. Since the downward deflected right aileron produces more lift, it also produces more drag, while the opposite left aileron has less lift and less drag. This added drag attempts to pull or veer the airplane's nose in the direction of the raised wing (right); that is, it tries to turn the airplane in the direction opposite to that desired. This undesired veering is referred to as adverse yaw.

26. What is "ground effect"? (AC 61-21A)

Ground effect occurs when an aircraft, operating approximately one wing span above the surface, experiences a reduction in induced drag and a resultant increase in the efficiency of the wing. This is due to the interference of the ground with the airflow patterns about the airplane or more specifically the wing's upwash, downwash, and wingtip vortices. In simple terms, ground effect is the cushioning or pushing effect of the air as it is compressed by an airplane flying close to the ground.

27. What major problems can be caused by ground effect? (AC 61-21A)

During landing, at a height of approximately one-tenth of a wing span above the surface, drag may be 40 percent less than when the airplane is operating out of ground effect. Therefore, any excess speed during the landing phase may result in a significant float distance. In such cases, if care is not exercised by the pilot, he/she may run out of runway and options at the same time.

During takeoff, due to the reduced drag in ground effect, the aircraft may seem capable of takeoff well below the recommended speed. However, as the airplane rises out of ground effect with a deficiency of speed, the greater induced drag may result in very marginal climb performance, or the inability of the airplane to fly at all. In extreme conditions, such as high temperature, high gross weight, and high-density altitude, the airplane may become airborne initially with a deficiency of speed and then settle back to the runway.

B. Weight and Balance

1. Define the following:

Empty weight—The airframe, engines, and all items of operating equipment that have fixed locations and are permanently installed in the aircraft. Includes hydraulic fluid, unusable fuel, and undrainable oil.

Gross weight—The maximum allowable weight of both the airplane and its contents.

Useful load—The weight of the pilot, copilot, passengers, baggage, usable fuel and drainable oil.

Arm—The horizontal distance in inches from the reference datum line to the center of gravity of the item.

Moment—The product of the weight of an item multiplied by its arm. Moments are expressed in pound-inches.

Center of gravity—The point about which an aircraft would balance if it were possible to suspend it at that point. Expressed in inches from datum.

Datum—An imaginary vertical plane or line from which all measurements of arm are taken. Established by the manufacturer.

2. What basic equation is used in all weight and balance problems to find the center of gravity location of an airplane and/or its components?

Weight x Arm = Moment

By rearrangement of this equation to the forms:

Weight = Moment ÷ arm

Arm (CG) = $\dfrac{\text{(Total) Moment}}{\text{(Total) Weight}}$

With any two known values, the third value can be found.

Remember: W A M
(Weight x Arm = Moment)

3. **What performance characteristics will be adversely affected when an aircraft has been overloaded?** (AC 61-21A)

    a. Takeoff speed increased

    b. Takeoff runway length increased

    c. Rate of climb reduced

    d. Maximum altitude capability reduced

    e. Operational range reduced

    f. Less maneuverability

    g. Less controllability

    h. Higher stall speed

    i. Higher approach speed

    j. Longer landing distance

4. **What effect does a forward center of gravity have on an aircraft's flight characteristics?** (AC 61-21A)

    Higher stall speed—stalling angle of attack is reached at a higher speed due to increased wing loading.

    Slower cruise speed—increased drag; greater angle of attack is required to maintain altitude.

    More stable—the center of gravity is farther forward from the center of pressure which increases longitudinal stability.

    Greater back elevator pressure required—longer takeoff roll; higher approach speeds and problems with landing flare.

5. **What effect does a rearward center of gravity have on an aircraft's flight characteristics?** (AC 61-21A)

    Lower stall speed—less wing loading.

    Higher cruise speed—reduced drag; smaller angle of attack is required to maintain altitude.

    Less stable—stall and spin recovery more difficult; the center of gravity is closer to the center of pressure, causing longitudinal instability.

6. What is the weight of aircraft fuel and oil? (AC 61-21A)

Aircraft fuel weighs 6 pounds per gallon. Aircraft oil weighs 7.5 pounds per gallon.

C. Aircraft Performance

1. What are some of the main elements of aircraft performance? (AC 61-21A)

    a. Takeoff and landing distance

    b. Rate of climb

    c. Ceiling

    d. Payload

    e. Range

    f. Speed

    g. Fuel economy

2. What factors affect the performance of an aircraft during takeoffs and landings? (AC 61-21A)

    a. Air density (density altitude)

    b. Surface wind

    c. Runway surface

    d. Upslope or downslope of runway

    e. Weight

3. How does surface wind affect takeoff and landing performance? (AC 61-21A)

For takeoffs the effect of wind is great. A headwind will allow an airplane to reach liftoff speed at a lower ground speed reducing the takeoff distance significantly. A tailwind will require the airplane to achieve a greater ground speed to attain the liftoff speed, increasing the effective takeoff distance.

For landings the effect of wind is also great. A headwind will shorten the landing distance by decreasing the ground speed at

Continued

which the airplane touches down. A tailwind will significantly increase the landing distance due to an increase in ground speed of the aircraft as it approaches and touches down.

4. How does weight affect takeoff and landing performance? (AC 61-21A)

Increased gross weight can have a significant effect on takeoff performance:

a. Higher liftoff speed;

b. Greater mass to accelerate (slow acceleration);

c. Increased retarding force (drag and ground friction); and

d. Longer takeoff distance.

The effect of gross weight on landing distance is that the airplane will require a greater speed to support the airplane at the landing angle of attack and lift coefficient resulting in an increased landing distance.

5. How does air density affect takeoff and landing performance? (AC 61-21A)

An increase in density altitude (decrease in air density) can also have the following effects on takeoff performance:

a. Greater takeoff TAS required;

b. Decreased thrust and reduced acceleration;

c. Longer takeoff ground roll; and

d. Decreased climb rate.

An increase in density altitude (decrease in air density) will increase the landing speed but will not alter the net retarding force. Thus, the airplane will land at the same indicated airspeed as normal but because of reduced air density the true airspeed will be greater. This will result in a longer minimum landing distance.

6. Define the term "density altitude." (AC 61-21A)

Density altitude is pressure altitude corrected for nonstandard temperature. It is the measurement of air density in terms of an altitude in a standard atmosphere.

7. How does air density affect aircraft performance? (AC 61-21A)

The density of the air has a direct effect on:

a. Lift produced by the wings;

b. Power output of the engine;

c. Propeller efficiency; and

d. Drag forces

8. What factors affect air density? (AC 61-21A)

a. Temperature

b. Altitude

c. Humidity

d. Barometric pressure

9. How do temperature, altitude, humidity and barometric pressure affect density altitude? (AC 61-21A)

Density altitude will *increase* (low air density) when one or more of the following occurs:

a. High air temperature

b. High altitude

c. High humidity

d. Low barometric pressure

Density altitude will *decrease* (high air density) when one or more of the following occurs:

a. Low air temperature

b. Low altitude

c. Low humidity

d. High barometric pressure

10. Define the following airplane performance speeds.
(AC 61-21A)

True airspeed (TAS)—the speed of the airplane in relation to the air mass in which it is flying.

Indicated airspeed (IAS)—the speed of the airplane as observed on the airspeed indicator. It is the airspeed without correction for instrument, position (or installation), or compressibility errors.

Calibrated airspeed (CAS)—the airspeed indicator reading corrected for position (or installation), and instrument errors.

Equivalent airspeed (EAS)—the airspeed indicator reading corrected for position (or installation), or instrument error, and for adiabatic compressible flow for the particular altitude.

11. Know the following speeds for your airplane!

V_{SO}—Stall speed in landing configuration; the calibrated power-off stalling speed or the minimum steady flight speed at which the airplane is controllable in the landing configuration.

V_S—Stall speed clean or in specified configuration; the calibrated power-off stalling speed or the minimum steady flight speed at which the airplane is controllable in a specified configuration.

V_Y—Best rate-of-climb speed; the calibrated airspeed at which the airplane will obtain the maximum increase in altitude per unit of time. This best rate-of-climb speed normally decreases slightly with altitude.

V_X—Best angle-of-climb speed; the calibrated airspeed at which the airplane will obtain the highest altitude in a given horizontal distance. This best angle-of-climb speed normally increases with altitude.

V_{LE}—Maximum landing gear extension speed; the maximum calibrated airspeed at which the airplane can be safely flown with the landing gear extended. This is a problem involving stability and controllability.

V_{LO}—Maximum landing gear operating speed; the maximum calibrated airspeed at which the landing gear can be safely extended or retracted. This is a problem involving the airloads imposed on the operating mechanism during extension or retraction of the gear.

V_{FE}—Maximum flap extension speed; the highest calibrated airspeed permissible with the wing flaps in a prescribed extended position. This is a problem involving the airloads imposed on the structure of the flaps.

V_A—Maneuvering speed; the calibrated design maneuvering airspeed. This is the maximum speed at which the limit load can be imposed (either by gusts or full deflection of the control surfaces) without causing structural damage.

V_{NO}—Normal operating speed; the maximum calibrated airspeed for normal operation or the maximum structural cruise speed. This is the speed above which exceeding the limit load factor may cause permanent deformation of the airplane structure.

V_{NE}—Never exceed speed; the calibrated airspeed which should *never* be exceeded. If flight is attempted above this speed, structural damage or structural failure may result.

12. What information can you obtain from the following charts? (AC 61-21A)

Takeoff Performance Charts

a. Normal takeoff ground run in feet

b. Obstacle clearance ground run in feet (50 feet)

Climb Performance Charts

a. Rate of climb under various conditions

b. Best climb airspeed under various conditions

Cruise Performance Charts

At various altitudes the following:

a. Recommended power settings

b. Percent brake horsepower

c. Rate of fuel consumption (gal/hr)

d. True airspeed

e. Hours of endurance with full tanks

f. Range in miles

Continued

Stall Speed Charts

Stall speeds with different flap settings and bank angles.

Landing Performance Charts

a. Normal landing distance

b. Landing distance to clear a 50-foot obstacle

13. Define the term "pressure altitude" and state why it is important. (AC 61-21A)

Pressure altitude is the altitude in the standard atmosphere corresponding to a particular pressure level. Pressure altitude is important as a basis for determining aircraft performance as well as for assigning flight levels to aircraft operating at high altitude (above 18,000 feet). Pressure altitude can be determined by setting the barometric scale of the altimeter to 29.92" Hg and reading the indicated altitude.

14. The following questions are designed to provide the pilot with a general review of the basic information they should know about their specific airplane before taking a flight check or review.

a. What is the normal climb-out speed?

b. What is the best rate-of-climb speed?

c. What is the best angle-of-climb speed?

d. What is the maximum flap extension speed?

e. What is the maximum gear extension speed?

f. What is the stall speed in the normal landing configuration?

g. What is the stall speed in the clean configuration?

h. What is the normal approach-to-land speed?

i. What is maneuvering speed?

j. What is red-line speed?

k. What engine-out glide speed will give you maximum range?

l. What is the make and horsepower of the engine?

m. How many usable gallons of fuel can you carry?

n. Where are the fuel tanks located, and what are their capacities?

o. What is the octane rating of the fuel used by your aircraft?

p. How do you drain the fuel sumps?

q. What are the minimum and maximum oil capacities?

r. What weight of oil is being used?

s. What is the maximum oil temperature and pressure?

t. Is the landing gear fixed, manual, hydraulic or electric? If retractable, what is the backup system for lowering the gear?

u. What is the maximum allowable/demonstrated crosswind component for the aircraft?

v. How many people will this aircraft carry safely with a full fuel load?

w. What is the maximum allowable weight the aircraft can carry with baggage in the baggage compartment?

x. What takeoff distance is required if a takeoff were made from a sea-level pressure altitude?

y. What is your maximum allowable useful load?

z. Solve a weight and balance problem for the flight you plan to make with one passenger at 170 pounds.

   i. Does your load fall within the weight and balance envelope?

   ii. What is the final gross weight?

   iii. How much fuel can be carried?

   iv. How much baggage can be carried with full fuel?

aa. Know the function of the various types of antennae on your aircraft.

Airplane
Systems

4

The following questions are in reference to the systems of a Cessna 152. For accuracy, you should review your aircraft owner's manual.

A. Aircraft and Engine Operations

1. What are the four main control surfaces and what are their functions? (AC 61-21A)

Elevators—The elevators control the movement of the airplane about its lateral axis. This motion is called pitch.

Ailerons—The ailerons control the airplane's movement about its longitudinal axis. This motion is called roll.

Rudder—The rudder controls movement of the airplane about its vertical axis. This motion is called yaw.

Trim Tabs—Trim tabs are small, adjustable hinged-surfaces on the aileron, rudder, or elevator control surfaces. They are labor-saving devices that enable the pilot to release manual pressure on the primary control.

2. How are the various flight controls operated?

The flight control surfaces are manually actuated through use of either a rod or cable system. A control wheel actuates the ailerons and elevator, and rudder/brake pedals actuate the rudder.

3. What are flaps and what is their function? (AC 61-21A)

The wing flaps are movable panels on the inboard trailing edges of the wings. They are hinged so that they may be extended down-ward into the flow of air beneath the wings to increase both lift and drag. Their purpose is to permit a slower airspeed and a steeper angle of descent during a landing approach. In some cases, they may also be used to shorten the takeoff distance.

4. Describe the landing gear system on this airplane.

The landing gear consists of a tricycle-type system utilizing two main wheels and a steerable nosewheel. Tubular spring steel main gear struts provide main gear shock absorption, while nose gear shock absorption is provided by a combination air/oil shock strut.

5. Describe the braking system on this aircraft.

Hydraulically actuated disc-type brakes are utilized on each main gear wheel. A hydraulic line connects each brake to a master cylinder located on each pilot's rudder pedals. By applying pressure to the top of either the pilot's or copilot's set of rudder pedals, the brakes may be applied.

6. How is steering accomplished on the ground?
(AC 61-23C)

Light airplanes are generally provided with nosewheel steering capabilities through a simple system of mechanical linkage connected to the rudder pedals. When a rudder pedal is depressed, a spring-loaded bungee (push-pull rod) connected to the pivotal portion of a nosewheel strut will turn the nosewheel.

7. What type of engine does your aircraft have?
(AC 61-23C)

A horizontally opposed four-cylinder, overhead-valve, air-cooled, carbureted engine. The engine is manufactured by Lycoming and rated at 110 HP.

8. What series of operations or events must occur in each cylinder of a typical four-stroke reciprocating engine in order for it to produce full power? (AC 61-23C)

The events that occur are:

Intake
Compression
Power
Exhaust

This cycle requires four strokes of the piston, two up and two down. Ignition of the fuel/air mixture at the end of the compression stroke adds a fifth event; consequently, the cycle of events is known as the four-stroke, five-event cycle principle.

9. What does the carburetor do? (AC 61-23C)

Carburetion may be defined as the process of mixing fuel and air in the correct proportions so as to form a combustible mixture. The carburetor vaporizes liquid fuel into small particles and then mixes it with air. It measures the airflow and meters fuel accordingly.

10. How does the carburetor heat system work? (AC 61-23C)

A carburetor heat valve, controlled by the pilot, allows unfiltered, heated air from a shroud located around an exhaust riser or muffler to be directed to the induction air manifold prior to the carburetor. Carburetor heat should be used anytime suspected or known carburetor icing conditions exist.

11. What change occurs to the fuel/air mixture when applying carburetor heat?

Normally, the introduction of heated air into the carburetor will result in a richer mixture. Warm air is less dense, resulting in less air for the same amount of fuel.

12. What does the throttle do? (AC 61-23C)

The throttle allows the pilot to manually control the amount of fuel/air charge entering the cylinders. This in turn regulates the engine speed and power.

13. What does the mixture control do? (AC 61-23C)

It regulates the fuel-to-air ratio. All airplane engines incorporate a device called a mixture control, by which the fuel/air ratio can be controlled by the pilot during flight. The purpose of a mixture control is to prevent the mixture from becoming too rich at high altitudes, due to decreasing air density. It is also used to lean the mixture during cross-country flights to conserve fuel and provide optimum power.

14. What type of ignition system does your airplane have? (AC 61-23C)

Engine ignition is provided by two engine-driven magnetos, and two spark plugs per cylinder. The ignition system is completely independent of the aircraft electrical system. The magnetos are engine-driven self-contained units supplying electrical current without using an external source of current. However, before they can produce current, the magnetos must be actuated, as the engine crankshaft is rotated by some other means. To accomplish this, the aircraft battery furnishes electrical power to operate a starter which, through a series of gears, rotates the engine crankshaft. This in turn actuates the armature of the magneto to produce the sparks for ignition of the fuel in each cylinder. After the engine starts, the starter system is disengaged, and the battery no longer contributes to the actual operation of the engine.

15. What are the two main advantages of a dual ignition system? (AC 61-23C)

a. Increased safety: in case one system fails the engine may be operated on the other until a landing is safely made.

b. More complete and even combustion of the mixture, and consequently, improved engine performance; i.e., the fuel/air mixture will be ignited on each side of the combustion chamber and burn toward the center.

16. What type of fuel system does your aircraft have?

The fuel system is a "gravity feed" system. Using gravity, the fuel flows from two wing fuel tanks to a fuel shutoff valve which, in the "on" position, allows fuel to flow through a strainer and then to the carburetor. From there, the fuel is mixed with air and then flows into the cylinders through the intake manifold tubes.

17. What purpose do fuel tank vents have?

As the fuel level in an aircraft fuel tank decreases, a vacuum would be created within the tank which would eventually result in a decreasing fuel flow and finally engine stoppage. Fuel system venting provides a way of replacing fuel with outside air, preventing formation of a vacuum.

18. Does your aircraft use a fuel pump?

No, the fuel is transferred from the wing tanks to the carburetor by the "gravity feed" system. The gravity system does not require a fuel pump because the fuel is always under positive pressure to the carburetor. For some aircraft where for some reason it is not possible to place the wings above the carburetor, or for which a greater pressure is required than what gravity feed can supply, it is necessary to utilize engine-driven fuel pumps and auxiliary fuel pumps as backups.

19. What type fuel does your aircraft require (minimum octane rating and color)?

The approved fuel grade used is 100LL and the color is blue.

20. Can other types of fuel be used if the specified grade is not available?

You may use fuel of a higher grade but only as a temporary solution. In no case should you ever use a fuel of a lower grade such as 80/87. If you must use a different grade of fuel, use a grade as close as possible to 100LL such as 100/130 or 115/145, and use it only for a short period of time.

21. What is the function of the manual primer, and how does it operate?

The manual primer's main function is to provide assistance in starting the engine. The primer draws fuel from the fuel strainer and injects it directly into the cylinder intake ports. This usually results in a quicker, more efficient engine start.

22. Describe the electrical system on your aircraft.

Electrical energy is provided by a 28-volt, direct-current system powered by an engine-driven 60-amp alternator and a 24-volt battery.

23. How are the circuits for the various electrical accessories within the aircraft protected?

Most of the electrical circuits in an airplane are protected from an overload condition by either circuit breakers or fuses or both. Circuit breakers perform the same function as fuses except that when an overload occurs, a circuit breaker can be reset.

24. The electrical system provides power for what equipment in an airplane?

Normally the following:

a. Radio equipment

b. Turn coordinator

c. Fuel gauges

d. Pitot heat

e. Landing light

f. Taxi light

g. Strobe lights

h. Interior lights

i. Instrument lights

j. Position lights

k. Flaps (maybe)

l. Stall warning system (maybe)

m. Oil temperature gauge

n. Electric fuel pump (maybe)

25. What does the ammeter indicate?

The ammeter indicates the flow of current, in amperes, from the alternator to the battery or from the battery to the electrical system. With the engine running and master switch on, the ammeter will indicate the charging rate to the battery. If the alternator has gone off-line and is no longer functioning, or the electrical load exceeds the output of the alternator, the ammeter indicates the discharge rate of the battery.

26. What function does the voltage regulator have?

The voltage regulator is a device which monitors system voltage, detects changes, and makes the required adjustments in the output of the alternator to maintain a constant regulated system voltage. It must do this at low RPM, such as during taxi, as well as at high RPM in flight. In a 28-volt system, it will maintain 28 volts ±0.5 volts.

27. How does the aircraft cabin heat work?

Fresh air, heated by an exhaust shroud, is directed to the cabin through a series of ducts.

28. How does the pilot control temperature in the cabin?

Temperature is controlled by mixing outside air (cabin air control) with heated air (cabin heat control) in a manifold near the cabin firewall. This air is then ducted to vents located on the cabin floor.

29. What are the two types of oil available for use in your airplane?

Mineral oil—Also known as nondetergent oil. It contains no additives. This type oil is normally used after an engine overhaul or when an aircraft engine is new, for engine break-in purposes.

Ashless dispersant—Mineral oil with additives. It has high antiwear properties along with multi-viscosity (ability to perform in a wide range of temperatures). It also picks up contamination and carbon particles and keeps them suspended so that buildups and sludge do not form in the engine.

B. System and Equipment Malfunctions

1. What causes "carburetor icing," and what are the first indications of its presence? (AC 61-23C)

The vaporization of fuel, combined with the expansion of air as it passes through the carburetor, causes a sudden cooling of the mixture. The temperature of the air passing through the carburetor may drop as much as 60°F within a fraction of a second. Water vapor is squeezed out by this cooling, and if the temperature in the carburetor reaches 32°F or below, the moisture will be deposited as frost or ice inside the carburetor. For airplanes with a fixed-pitch propeller, the first indication of carburetor icing is loss of RPM. For airplanes with controllable-pitch (constant-speed) propellers, the first indication is usually a drop in manifold pressure.

2. What conditions are favorable for carburetor icing? (AC 61-23C)

On dry days, or when the temperature is well below freezing, the moisture in the air is not generally enough to cause trouble. But if the temperature is between 20°F and 70°F with visible moisture or high humidity, the pilot should be alert. Also, during low or closed throttle settings, an engine is particularly susceptible to carburetor icing.

3. What is "detonation"? (AC 61-23C)

Detonation is caused when the fuel/air mixture is subjected to a combination of excessively high temperatures and high pressure within the cylinder, resulting in an instantaneous burning (explosion) of the mixture. This form of combustion causes a definite loss of power, engine overheating, preignition and, if allowed to continue, physical damage to the engine.

4. What action should be taken if detonation is suspected? (AC 61-23C)

Corrective action for detonation may be accomplished by adjusting any of the engine controls which will reduce both temperature and pressure of the fuel air charge.

a. Reduce power.

b. Reduce the climb rate for better cooling.

c. Enrich the fuel/air mixture.

d. Open cowl flaps if available.

Also, ensure that the airplane has been serviced with the proper grade of fuel.

5. What is "preignition"? (AC 61-23C)

Preignition is defined as ignition of the fuel prior to normal ignition, or ignition before the electrical arcing occurs at the spark plugs. Preignition may be caused by excessively hot exhaust valves, carbon particles or spark plug electrodes heated to an incandescent or glowing state. In most cases these local "hot spots" are caused by the high temperatures encountered during detonation.

6. What actions should be taken if preignition is suspected? (AC 61-23C)

Corrective actions for preignition include any type of engine operation which would promote cooling such as:

a. Reduce power.

b. Reduce the climb rate for better cooling.

c. Enrich the fuel/air mixture.

d. Open cowl flaps if available.

7. During the before-takeoff runup, you switch the magnetos from the "BOTH" position to the "RIGHT" position and notice there is no RPM drop. What condition does this indicate?

The left P-lead is not grounding, or the engine has been running only on the right magneto because the left magneto has totally failed.

8. Interpret the following ammeter indications.

a. Ammeter indicates a right deflection (positive).

i. *After starting*—Power from the battery used for starting is being replenished by the alternator; or, if a full-scale charge is indicated for more than 1 minute, the starter is still engaged and a shutdown is indicated.

ii. *During flight*—A faulty voltage regulator is causing the alternator to overcharge the battery. Reset the system and if the condition continues, terminate the flight as soon as possible.

b. Ammeter indicates a left deflection (negative).

i. *After starting*—It is normal during start. At other times this indicates the alternator is not functioning or an overload condition exists in the system. The battery is not receiving a charge.

ii. *During flight*—The alternator is not functioning or an overload exists in the system. The battery is not receiving a charge. Possible causes: the master switch was accidentally shut off, or the alternator circuit breaker tripped.

9. What action should be taken if the ammeter indicates a continuous discharge while in flight?

The alternator has quit producing a charge, so the alternator circuit breaker should be checked and reset if necessary. If this does not correct the problem, the following should be accomplished:

a. The alternator should be turned off; pull the circuit breaker (the field circuit will continue to draw power from the battery).

b. All electrical equipment not essential to flight should be turned off (the battery is now the only source of electrical power).

c. The flight should be terminated and a landing made as soon as possible.

10. What action should be taken if the ammeter indicates a continuous charge while in flight (more than two needle widths)?

If a continuous excessive rate of charge were allowed for any extended period of time, the battery would overheat and evaporate the electrolyte at an excessive rate. A possible explosion of the battery could result. Also, electronic components in the electrical system would be adversely affected by higher than normal voltage. Protection is provided by an overvoltage sensor which will shut the alternator down if an excessive voltage is detected. If this should occur the following should be done:

a. The alternator should be turned off; pull the circuit breaker (the field circuit will continue to draw power from the battery).

b. All electrical equipment not essential to flight should be turned off (the battery is now the only source of electrical power).

c. The flight should be terminated and a landing made as soon as possible.

11. During a cross-country flight you notice that the oil pressure is low, but the oil temperature is normal. What is the problem and what action should be taken?

A low oil pressure in flight could be the result of any one of several problems, the most common being that of insufficient oil. If the oil temperature continues to remain normal, a clogged oil pressure relief valve or an oil pressure gauge malfunction could be the culprit. In any case, a landing at the nearest airport is advisable to check for the cause of trouble.

12. What procedures should be followed concerning a partial loss of power in flight?

If a partial loss of power occurs, the first priority is to establish and maintain a suitable airspeed (best glide airspeed if necessary). Then, select an emergency landing area and remain within gliding distance. As time allows, attempt to determine the cause and correct it.

Continued

Complete the following checklist:

a. Check the carburetor heat.

b. Check the amount of fuel in each tank and switch fuel tanks if necessary.

c. Check the fuel selector valve's current position.

d. Check the mixture control.

e. Check that the primer control is all the way in and locked.

f. Check the operation of the magnetos in all three positions; both, left or right.

13. What procedures should be followed if an engine fire develops in flight?

In the event of an engine fire in flight, the following procedures should be used:

a. Set the mixture control to "Idle cutoff."

b. Set the fuel selector valve to "Off."

c. Turn the master switch to "Off."

d. Set the cabin heat and air vents to "Off"; leave the overhead vents "On."

e. Establish an airspeed of 100 KIAS and increase the descent, if necessary, to find an airspeed that will provide for an incombustible mixture.

f. Execute a forced landing procedures checklist.

14. What procedures should be followed if an engine fire develops on the ground during starting?

Continue to attempt an engine start as a start will cause flames and excess fuel to be sucked back through the carburetor.

a. If the engine starts:

  i. Increase the power to a higher RPM for a few moments; and

  ii. Shut down the engine and inspect it.

b. If the engine does not start:

  i. Set the throttle to the "Full" position.

    ii. Set the mixture control to "Idle cutoff."

    iii. Continue to try an engine start in an attempt to put out the fire by vacuum.

  c. If the fire continues:

    i. Turn the ignition switch to "Off."

    ii. Turn the master switch to "Off."

    iii. Set the fuel selector to "Off."

In all cases, evacuate the aircraft and obtain a fire extinguisher and/or assistance.

C. Flight Instruments

Pitot/static system

1. What instruments operate off of the pitot/static system? (AC 61-27C)

Altimeter, Vertical Speed, and Airspeed Indicator.

2. How does an altimeter work? (AC 61-27C)

Aneroid wafers expand and contract as atmospheric pressure changes, and through a shaft and gear linkage, rotate pointers on the dial of the instrument.

3. What are the limitations of a pressure altimeter? (AC 61-27C)

Nonstandard pressure and temperature; temperature variations expand or contract the atmosphere and raise or lower pressure levels that the altimeter senses.

On a warm day—The pressure level is higher than on a standard day. The altimeter indicates lower than actual altitude.

On a cold day—The pressure level is lower than on a standard day. The altimeter indicates higher than actual altitude.

Continued

Changes in surface pressure also affect pressure levels at altitude.

Higher than standard pressure—The pressure level is higher than on a standard day. The altimeter indicates lower than actual altitude.

Lower than standard pressure—The pressure level is lower than on a standard day. The altimeter indicates higher than actual altitude.

Remember: High to low or hot to cold, look out below!

4. Define and state how you would determine the following altitudes. (AC 61-27C)

Indicated altitude
Pressure altitude
True altitude
Density altitude
Absolute altitude

Indicated altitude—Read off the face of the altimeter.

Pressure altitude—Indicated altitude with 29.92" Hg set in the Kollsman window.

True altitude—Height above sea level. Use the flight computer.

Density altitude—Pressure altitude corrected for nonstandard temperature. Use the flight computer.

Absolute altitude—Height above ground. Subtract the terrain elevation from true altitude.

5. How does the airspeed indicator operate? (AC 61-27C)

It measures the difference between ram pressure from the pitot head and atmospheric pressure from the static source.

6. What is the limitation of the airspeed indicator? (AC 61-27C)

The airspeed indicator is subject to proper flow of air in the pitot/static system.

7. What are the errors of the airspeed indicator?
(AC 61-27C)

Position error—Caused by the static ports sensing erroneous static pressure; slipstream flow causes disturbances at the static port preventing actual atmospheric pressure measurement. It varies with airspeed, altitude and configuration, and may be a plus or minus value.

Density error—Changes in altitude and temperature are not compensated for by the instrument.

Compressibility error—Caused by the packing of air into the pitot tube at high airspeeds, resulting in higher than normal indications. It is usually not a factor at slower speeds.

8. What are the different types of aircraft speeds?
(AC 61-27C)

Indicated airspeed (IAS)—read off the instrument.

Calibrated airspeed (CAS)—IAS corrected for instrument and position errors; obtained from the Pilot's Operating Handbook or off the face of the instrument.

Equivalent airspeed (EAS)—CAS corrected for adiabatic compressible flow at altitude.

True airspeed (TAS)—EAS corrected for nonstandard temperature and pressure; obtained from the flight computer, POH or A/S indicator slide computer.

Groundspeed (GS)—TAS corrected for wind; speed across ground; use the flight computer.

9. Are the color bands on an airspeed indicator indicated airspeeds or calibrated airspeeds? (AC 61-27C)

Airspeed indicators indicate calibrated airspeed (usually in mph) if manufactured in 1975 or before, and indicated airspeed (usually in knots) if manufactured in 1976 or after.

10. What airspeed limitations apply to the color-coded marking system of the airspeed indicator? (AC 61-23C)

White Arc .... flap operating range

Lower A/S Limit White Arc .... V_{SO} (stall speed landing configuration)

Upper A/S Limit White Arc .... V_{FE} (maximum flap extension speed)

Green Arc .... normal operating range

Lower A/S Limit Green Arc .... V_S (stall speed clean or specified configuration)

Upper A/S Limit Green Arc .... V_{NO} (normal operations speed or maximum structural cruise speed)

Yellow Arc .... Caution Range (operations in smooth air only)

Red Line .... V_{NE} (maximum speed for operations in smooth air only)

11. How does the vertical speed indicator work? (AC 61-27C)

Changing pressures expand or contract a diaphragm connected to the indicating needle through gears and levers. The Vertical Speed Indicator (VSI) is connected to the static pressure line through a calibrated leak; the VSI measures differential pressure.

12. What are the limitations of the vertical speed indicator? (AC 61-27C)

It is not accurate until the aircraft is stabilized. Sudden or abrupt changes in the aircraft attitude will cause erroneous instrument readings as airflow fluctuates over the static port. These changes are not reflected immediately by the VSI due to a calibrated leak.

D. Vacuum/Gyroscopic System

1. What instruments contain gyroscopes? (AC 61-23C)

a. the turn coordinator

b. the directional gyro (heading indicator)

c. the attitude indicator (artificial horizon)

2. What instruments operate off of the vacuum system?
(AC 61-27C)

Normally the attitude indicator and the directional gyro. The turn coordinator could also be vacuum-driven depending on the particular aircraft. The industry standard dictates that the artificial horizon and directional gyro be vacuum-driven and the turn coordinator be electrically driven. However, in some systems all three can be electrically driven.

3. How does the vacuum system operate? (AC 61-27C)

An engine-driven vacuum pump provides suction which pulls air from the instrument case. Normal pressure entering the case is directed against rotor vanes to turn the rotor (gyro) at high speed, much like a water wheel or turbine operates. Air is drawn into the instrument through a filter from the cockpit and eventually vented outside. Vacuum values vary but provide rotor speeds from 8,000 to 18,000 RPM.

4. How does the attitude indicator work? (AC 61-27C)

A gyro stabilizes the artificial horizon parallel to the real horizon

5. What are the limitations of an attitude indicator?
(AC 61-23C)

The pitch and bank limits depend upon the make and model of the instrument. Limits in the banking plane are usually from 100 degrees to 110 degrees, and the pitch limits are usually from 60 to 70 degrees. If either limit is exceeded, the instrument will tumble or spill and will give incorrect indications until reset. A number of modern attitude indicators will not tumble.

6. What are the errors of the attitude indicator?
(AC 61-27C)

Errors in both pitch and bank occur during normal coordinated turns. These errors are caused by the movement of pendulous vanes by centrifugal force resulting in precession of the gyro

Continued

toward the inside of the turn. The greatest error occurs in 180° of turn. In a 180° turn to the right, on rollout the attitude indicator will indicate a slight climb and turn to the left. Acceleration and deceleration errors cause the attitude indicator to indicate a climb when the aircraft is accelerated and a descent when the aircraft is decelerated.

7. How does the directional gyro operate? (AC 61-27C)

A gyro stabilizes the heading indicator. The speed of the gyro is usually 10,000 to 18,000 RPM.

8. What are the limitations of the directional gyro? (AC 61-23C)

The bank and pitch limits of the heading indicator vary with the particular design and make of instrument. On some heading indicators found in light airplanes, the limits are approximately 55 degrees of pitch and 55 degrees of bank. When either of these attitude limits is exceeded, the instrument "tumbles" or "spills" and no longer gives the correct indication until reset. After spilling, it may be reset with the caging knob. Many of the modern instruments used are designed in such a manner that they will not tumble.

9. What error is the directional gyro subject to? (AC 61-27C)

Precession of the gyro.

E. Electric/Gyroscopic System

1. What instruments operate on this system? (AC 61-27C)

Turn Coordinator—In some aircraft this system could also operate the artificial horizon and directional gyro (refer to vacuum/gyro system questions #1 and #2, section D).

2. How does the turn coordinator operate? (AC 61-27C)

The turn part of the instrument uses precession to indicate direction and approximate rate of turn. A gyro reacts by trying to move in reaction to the force applied thus moving the needle or miniature aircraft in proportion to the rate of turn. The slip/skid indicator is a liquid-filled tube with a ball that reacts to centrifugal force and gravity.

3. What information does the turn coordinator provide? (AC 61-27C)

The miniature aircraft of the turn coordinator displays the rate of turn and rate of roll. The ball in the tube indicates a slipping or skidding condition.

Slip—Ball on the inside of turn; not enough rate of turn for the amount of bank.

Skid—Ball to the outside of turn; too much rate of turn for the amount of bank.

4. What limitations apply to the turn coordinator? (AC 61-27C)

A spring is attached between the instrument case and the gyro assembly in order to hold the gyro upright when no precession force is applied. Tension on the spring may be adjusted to calibrate the instrument for a given rate of turn. The spring restricts the amount of gyro tilt. Stops prevent the gyro assembly from tilting more than 45 degrees to either side of the upright position.

F. Magnetic Compass

1. How does the magnetic compass work? (AC 61-27C)

Magnets mounted on the compass card align themselves parallel to the earth's lines of magnetic force.

2. What limitations does the magnetic compass have? (AC 61-27C)

The float assembly of the compass is balanced on a pivot, which allows free rotation of the card, and allows it to tilt at an angle up to 18 degrees.

3. What are the various compass errors? (AC 61-27C)

Oscillation error—Erratic movement of the compass card caused by turbulence or rough control technique.

Deviation error—Due to electrical and magnetic disturbances in the aircraft.

Variation error—Angular difference between true and magnetic north; reference isogonic lines of variation.

Dip errors:

Acceleration error—On east or west headings, while accelerating, the magnetic compass shows a turn to the north, and when decelerating, it shows a turn to the south.

Remember: ANDS

A ccelerate
N orth
D ecelerate
S outh

Northerly turning error—The compass leads in the south half of a turn, and lags in the north half of a turn.

Remember: UNOS

U ndershoot
N orth
O vershoot
S outh

Cross-Country
Flight Planning

5

A. Navigation

1. What are three common ways to navigate?

To navigate successfully, pilots must know their approximate position at all times or be able to determine it whenever they wish. Position may be determined by:

a. Pilotage (by reference to visible landmarks);

b. Dead reckoning (by computing direction and distance from a known position); or

c. Radio navigation (by use of radio aids).

2. What type of aeronautical charts are available for use in VFR navigation? (AC 61-23C)

a. *Sectional Aeronautical Charts*—These charts are designed for visual navigation and are named for a principle city or geographic feature. One inch on a sectional chart is equal to a distance of approximately 7 nautical miles. They are revised every 6 months.

b. *VFR Terminal Area Charts*—Large scale charts, primarily for use on VFR flights in highly congested areas with more topographical detail than other charts. They are normally available for areas that have airspace designated as Class B airspace. One inch on a terminal area chart is equal to approximately 3.5 nautical miles. They are revised every 6 months.

c. *World Aeronautical Charts*—These charts are designed to provide a standard series of aeronautical charts, covering land areas of the world, at a size and scale convenient for navigation by moderate-speed aircraft. One inch on a WAC chart is equal to 13.7 nautical miles. They are revised annually.

3. Be capable of locating the following items on a sectional chart:

Abandoned airports
Air Defense Identification Zone (ADIZ)
Airport elevation
Airports with a rotating beacon
Airports with lighting facilities
Airports with services
Alert Area
Approach Control frequencies
ATIS
Class B airspace
Class C airspace
Class D airspace
Class D airspace ceiling
Class E airspace (without operating control tower)
Class E airspace (controlled airspace 700 foot floor)
Class E airspace (controlled airspace 1,200 foot floor)
Class E airspace extensions to Class D airspace
Class G airspace
CTAF
Flight Service Station frequencies
Glider operating area
Hard surfaced runway airports
HIWAS
Isogonic lines
Maximum elevation figures
Military Airports
Military Training Routes
No fixed-wing Special VFR available
Non-hard surfaced runways
Non-directional radio beacons
Non-tower controlled airport
Obstructions above 1,000 feet AGL
Obstructions below 1,000 feet AGL
Parachute Jumping Area
Part-time lighting
Pilot Controlled Lighting
Private airports
Prohibited area

Restricted area
Runway length
Special VFR not authorized
UNICOM frequencies
Victor airways
Visual check points
VORTAC
Warning area
TRSA (Terminal Radar Service Area) if available
TWEB

4. What is an "isogonic line"? (AC 61-23C)

Shown on most aeronautical charts as broken red lines, isogonic lines connect points of equal magnetic variation. They show the amount and direction of magnetic variation, which from time to time may vary.

5. What is "magnetic variation"? (AC 61-23C)

Magnetic variation is the error induced by the difference in location of true north and magnetic north. It is expressed in east or west variation.

6. How do you convert a true direction to a magnetic direction? (AC 61-23C)

To convert from TRUE (measured from the meridians on the chart) to MAGNETIC, note the variation shown by the nearest isogonic line.

If variation is west, add; if east, subtract.

Remember: East is Least (Subtract)
               West is Best (Add)

7. What are lines of latitude and longitude? (AC 61-23C)

Circles parallel to the equator (lines running east and west), parallels of latitude, enable us to measure distance in degrees latitude north or south of the equator. Meridians of longitude are

Continued

drawn from the North Pole to the South Pole and are at right angles to the equator. The "Prime Meridian," which passes through Greenwich, England, is used as the zero line from which measurements are made in degrees east and west to 180°. The 48 conterminous states of the United States lie between 25 degrees and 49 degrees north latitude and between 67 degrees and 125 degrees west longitude.

8. What is "magnetic deviation"? (AC 61-23C)

Because of magnetic influences within the airplane itself (electrical circuits, radios, lights, tools, engine, magnetized metal parts, etc.) the compass needle is frequently deflected from its normal reading. This deflection is called deviation. Deviation is different for each airplane, and also varies for different headings of the same airplane. The deviation value may be found on a deviation card located in the airplane.

9. Name several types of radio aids to air navigation.

a. VOR (Very High Frequency Omnidirectional Range)

b. NDB (Nondirectional Radio Beacon)

c. RNAV (Area Navigation)

d. DME (Distance Measuring Equipment)

e. LORAN (Long Range Navigation)

f. GPS (Global Positioning System)

10. What is a "VOR" or "VORTAC"?

VORs are VHF radio stations that project radials in all directions (360°) from the station, like spokes from the hub of a wheel. Each of these radials is denoted by its outbound magnetic direction. Almost all VOR stations will also be VORTACs. A VORTAC (VOR-Tactical Air Navigation), provides the standard bearing information of a VOR plus distance information to pilots of airplanes which have distance measuring equipment (DME).

11. Within what frequency range do VORs operate? (AC 61-23C)

Transmitting frequencies of omnirange stations are in the VHF (very high frequency) band between 108 and 118 MHz, which are immediately below aviation communication frequencies.

12. What is a VOR "radial"? (AC 61-23C)

A "radial" is defined as a line of magnetic bearing extending from an omnidirectional range (VOR). A VOR projects 360 radials from the station. These radials are always identified by their direction "from" the station. Regardless of heading, an aircraft on the 360° radial will always be located due north of the station.

13. How are VOR NAVAIDs classified? (AIM 1-1-8)

VORs are classified by their basic operational use:

a. *Terminal Class VORs* are primarily for use in terminal areas where the VOR is located on the airport or near it for use in instrument approaches.

b. *Low-Class VORs* are used along the low-altitude Victor airways.

c. *High-Class VORs* define the high-altitude jet routes, as well as low-altitude Victor airways.

14. What reception distances can be expected from the various class VORs? (AIM 1-1-8)

Terminal	below 12,000 feet	25 miles
Low-Altitude	below 18,000 feet	40 miles
High-Altitude	1,000 to 14,499 feet	40 miles
High-Altitude	14,500 to 17,999 feet	100 miles
High-Altitude	18,000 to 45,000 feet	130 miles
High-Altitude	above 45,000 feet	100 miles

15. What limitations, if any, apply to VOR reception distances? (AIM 1-1-3)

VORs are subject to line-of-sight restrictions, and the range varies proportionally to the altitude of the receiving equipment.

16. What are some advantages in using VOR navigation? (AC 61-23C)

a. *Static-free reception*—VORs transmit in the VHF frequency range resulting in relatively static-free reception. Thunderstorms and other weather phenomena may cause static and interference which limit the accuracy of other forms of navigation.

b. *Very accurate*—The accuracy of course alignment of the VOR is excellent, being generally ±1°.

c. A flight can be made to a VOR from any direction by flying the course to the station. A flight may be made to any destination from the station by selecting the proper radial. When in range of two or more VORs, a fix may be determined quickly and easily by taking bearings on the stations and determining position on a chart.

d. *Wind drift correction*—Wind drift is taken care of automatically by flying whatever heading is necessary to keep the course deviation needle centered.

17. What is an "NDB"? (AIM 1-1-2)

A nondirectional beacon; a low- to medium-frequency radio beacon transmits nondirectional signals whereby the pilot of an aircraft properly equipped can determine bearings and "home" or "track" to the station.

18. Within what frequency range do NDBs operate? (AIM 1-1-2)

These facilities normally operate in the frequency band of 190 to 535 kHz (immediately below AM broadcast bands) and transmit a continuous carrier with either 400 or 1020 Hz modulation. All radio beacons, except compass locators, transmit a continuous three-letter identification code.

19. **What is "ADF"?** (AC 61-23C)

Automatic Direction Finder; many airplanes are equipped with ADF radio receivers which operate in the low- and medium-frequency bands. By tuning to low-frequency radio stations such as NDBs or commercial broadcast stations, a pilot may use ADF for navigation in cross-country flying. The most common use of ADF is that of "homing" by flying the needle to a station.

20. **What are some advantages in using ADF for navigation?** (AC 61-23C)

a. The low cost of equipment and usually very low maintenance.

b. Low-frequency ranges under normal conditions are usable for distances of 50 to 100 miles, and sometimes greater. They can be received at low altitudes and on the ground. The signal is not dependent on line of sight, like VHF or UHF, but follows the curvature of the earth.

21. **What are some of the limitations of ADF navigation?** (AC 61-23C)

a. It does not automatically account for wind drift.

b. It is susceptible to difficulties from thunderstorms and static.

c. It is susceptible to other forms of interference, such as twilight effect, terrain effect, and shoreline effect.

22. **What is "RNAV"?** (AIM Glossary)

RNAV is an abbreviation for Area Navigation and is a form of navigation that permits aircraft, properly equipped, to operate on any desired course within the coverage of station-referenced navigation signals. This form of navigation allows a pilot to select a more direct course to a destination by not requiring overflight of ground-based navigational aids. Navigation is to selected "way-points" instead of VORs. A "waypoint" is created by simply moving the VOR to a point along the route of flight desired.

23. What is "DME"? (AIM 1-1-7)

Distance Measuring Equipment—aircraft equipped with DME are provided with distance and ground speed information when receiving a VORTAC or TACAN facility. In the operation of DME, paired pulses at a specific spacing are sent out from the aircraft and are received at the ground station. The ground station then transmits paired pulses back to the aircraft at the same pulse spacing but on a different frequency. The time required for the round trip of this signal exchange is measured in the airborne DME unit and translated into distance and ground speed.

24. What is "LORAN"? (AIM 1-1-16)

Long Range Navigation—a navigational system based upon measurement of the difference in time of arrival of pulses of radio signals radiated by a group of transmitter stations which are separated by hundreds of miles. A LORAN receiver is basically an on-board computer capable of determining the aircraft's position based on the measurement of the time-differential receipt of these different signals. LORAN receivers also have computer memory capable of storing information, and useful programs such as:

a. Airport locations

b. Location of airspace such as Class B airspace

c. Navigational aids (VORs, NDBs)

d. Navigational fixes (intersections, waypoints)

e. Ability to continuously compute nearest airport, or bearing to for emergency use

f. Distance from starting point and destination

g. Time en route and estimated time to station

h. Ground speed and true airspeed

25. What is "GPS"? (AIM Glossary)

Global Positioning System —a space-based radio positioning, navigation, and time-transfer system. The system provides highly accurate position and velocity information, and precise time, on a continuous global basis to an unlimited number of properly equipped users. The system is unaffected by weather, and provides a worldwide common grid reference system. The GPS concept is predicated upon accurate and continuous knowledge of the spatial position of each satellite in the system with respect to time and distance from a transmitting satellite to the user. The GPS receiver automatically selects appropriate signals from satellites in view and translates these into three-dimentional position, velocity, and time. System accuracy for civil users is normally 100 meters horizontally.

B. Flight Computers and Basic Calculations

1. Before attempting a cross-country flight, a pilot will need to know how to make common calculations for time, speed, distance, amount of fuel required, as well as basic wind calculations. Solve the following:

Time, speed and distance problems:

a. If time equals 25 minutes and distance equals 47 NM, what will speed be?

b. If distance equals 84 NM and speed equals 139 knots, what will time be?

c. If speed is 85 knots and time is 51 minutes, what will the distance be?

   a. 113 knots

   b. 36 minutes

   c. 72 NM

Fuel consumption problems:

a. If gallons-per-hour is 9.3 and time is 1 hour, 27 minutes, how many gallons will be consumed?

b. If time is 2 hours, 13 minutes and gallons consumed is 32, what will the gallons-per-hour be?

Continued

c. If gallons consumed is 38 and gallons-per-hour is 10.8, what will the time be?

   a. 13.5 gallons

   b. 14.4 GPH

   c. 3 hours, 31 minutes

True airspeed problems:

a. If altitude is 10,000 feet, temperature is 0°C, and IAS is 115, what will the TAS be?

b. If IAS is 103, altitude is 6,000 feet, and the temperature is -10°C, what will the TAS be?

c. If the temperature is 40°F, the IAS is 115, and the altitude is 11,000 feet, what will the TAS be?

   a. 135 TAS

   b. 110 TAS

   c. 139 TAS

Density altitude problems:

a. If pressure altitude is 1,500 feet and the temperature is 35°C, what will the density altitude be?

b. If pressure altitude is 5,000 feet and the temperature is -10°C, what will the density altitude be?

c. If the pressure altitude is 2,000 feet and the temperature is 30°C, what will the density altitude be?

   a. 4,100 feet

   b. 3,100 feet

   c. 4,200 feet

Conversion problems:

a. 100 nautical miles = _____ statute miles

b. 12 quarts oil = _____ pounds

c. 45 gallons fuel = _____ pounds

d. 80°F = _____ °C

e. 20 knots = _____ miles per hour

  a. 115 SM

  b. 22.5 pounds

  c. 270 pounds

  d. 26.6°C

  e. 23 MPH

Ground speed/true heading problems:

a. If wind direction is 220, wind speed is 030, true course is 146, and TAS is 135, what will ground speed and true heading be?

b. If wind direction is 240, wind speed is 025, true course is 283 and TAS is 165, what will ground speed and true heading be?

c. If wind direction is 060, wind speed is 030, true course is 036 and TAS is 140, what will ground speed and true heading be?

  a. Ground speed is 124, true heading is 158.

  b. Ground speed is 146, true heading is 277.

  c. Ground speed is 112, true heading is 041.

2. Flight log example, VFR flight plan:

Careful preflight planning is extremely important. A wise pilot ensures a successful cross-country flight by getting a good weather briefing and completing a flight log before flight.

  a. Get a weather briefing from a Flight Service Station. Write it down.

  b. Draw course lines and mark checkpoints on the chart.

  c. Enter checkpoints on the log.

  d. Enter NAVAIDs on the log.

  e. Enter VOR courses on the log.

Continued

f. Enter altitude on the log.

g. Enter the wind (direction/velocity) and temperature on the log.

h. Measure the true course on the chart and enter it on the log.

i. Compute the true airspeed and enter it on the log.

j. Compute the WCA and GS and enter them on the log.

k. Determine variation from chart and enter it on the log.

l. Determine deviation from compass correction card and enter it on the log.

m. Enter compass heading on the log.

n. Measure distances on the chart and enter them on the log.

o. Figure ETE and ETA and enter them on the log.

p. Calculate fuel burn and usage; enter them on the log.

q. Compute weight and balance.

r. Compute takeoff and landing performance.

s. Complete a Flight Plan form.

t. File the Flight Plan with FSS.

3. Diversion to Alternate/Lost Procedures:

a. What actions should be taken if you become disoriented or lost on a cross-country flight?

Condition I: plenty of fuel and weather conditions good.

i. Straighten up and fly right. Fly a specific heading in a direction you believe to be correct (or circle, if unsure); don't wander aimlessly.

ii. If you have been flying a steady compass heading and keeping a relatively accurate navigation log, it's not likely you will have a problem locating your position.

iii. If several VORs are within reception distance, use them for a cross-bearing to determine position (even a single VOR can be of enormous help in narrowing down your possible position); or, fly to the station—there's no doubt where you are then.

iv. Use knowledge of your last known position, elapsed time, approximate wind direction and ground speed, to establish how far you may have traveled since your last checkpoint.

v. Use this distance as a radius and draw a semicircle ahead of your last known position on chart. For example, you estimate your ground speed at 120 knots. If you have been flying 20 minutes since your last checkpoint, then the no-wind radius of your semicircle is 40 miles projected along the direction of your estimated track.

vi. If still unsure of your position, loosen up the eyeballs and start some first-class pilotage. Look for something big. Don't concern yourself with the minute or trivial at this point. Often, there will be linear features such as rivers, mountain ranges, or prominent highways and railroads that are easy to identify. You can use them simply as references for orientation purposes and thus find them of great value in fixing your approximate position.

Condition II: low on fuel; weather deteriorating; inadequate experience; darkness imminent; and/or equipment malfunctioning.

Get it on the ground! Most accidents are the product of mistakes which have multiplied over a period of time and getting lost is no exception: don't push your luck. It may well be that in doing so, you have added the final mistake which will add another figure to the accident statistics. If terrain or other conditions make landing impossible at the moment, don't waste time, for it is of the essence: don't search for the perfect field—anything usable will do. Remember, most people on the ground know where they are, and you know that you do not.

b. If it becomes apparent that you cannot locate your position, what action is recommended at this point?

The FAA recommends the use of the "4 Cs":

i. Climb—The higher altitude allows better communication capability as well as better visual range for identification of landmarks.

Continued

    ii. Communicate—Use the system. Use 121.5 MHz if no other frequency produces results. It is guarded by FSS's, control towers, military towers, approach control facilities, and Air Route Traffic Control Centers.

    iii. Confess—Once communications are established, let them know your problem.

    iv. Comply—Follow instructions.

c. What is a "DF Steer"? (AIM Glossary)

It is a service provided to aircraft by ground facilities (FSS) equipped with direction-finding equipment. Aircraft in distress or other aircraft which request the service will be given a series of headings which will lead the aircraft to a predetermined point such as the DF station or an airport. The procedure is as follows:

    i. The pilot calls the VHF/DF station or FSS.

    ii. The VHF/DF station requests the pilot to transmit for 10 seconds; they determine his/her position.

    iii. The VHF/DF station provides a no wind course to the station.

    iv. The procedure may be repeated several times as necessary to bring the pilot to the station.

d. While en route on a cross-country flight, weather has deteriorated and it becomes necessary to divert to an alternate airport. What is the recommended procedure?

    i. Mark your present position on the chart. It is also advisable to write the current time next to this mark.

    ii. Establish a general direction to the alternate and turn to it immediately.

    iii. As time permits, determine distance, ground speed, and estimated time en route to the alternate.

Note: This is a very common checkride procedure, be prepared to do this.

C. Radio Communications

1. What frequencies are allocated for use by aviation in the VHF frequency band? (AC 61-23C)

The VHF frequencies allocated for aviation use are between 108 MHz and 136 MHz. The frequencies 108 MHz to 117.95 MHz are allocated to VHF air navigation radio aids. The frequencies 118 MHz to 136 MHz are generally used for Air Traffic Control and communication between pilots and ground facilities.

2. What is the universal VHF "Emergency" frequency? (AC 61-23C)

121.5 MHz; this frequency is guarded by federal towers, most military towers, Flight Service Stations, and radar facilities.

3. What bandwidths are used for ground control frequencies? (AC 61-23C)

The majority of ground control frequencies are in the 121.6 to 121.9 MHz bandwidth.

4. What is a "CTAF"? (AIM 4-1-9)

A CTAF (Common Traffic Advisory Frequency) is a frequency designated for the purpose of carrying out airport advisory practices while operating to or from an airport without an operating control tower. The CTAF may be a UNICOM, MULTICOM, FSS or TOWER frequency and is identified in appropriate aeronautical publications.

5. What is "UNICOM" and what frequencies are designated for its use? (AC 61-23C)

UNICOM is a nongovernment communication facility which may provide airport information at certain airports. Airports other than those with a control tower/FSS on airport will normally use 122.700, 122.725, 122.800, 122.975, 123.000, 123.050, and 123.075 MHz. Airports with a control tower or an FSS on airport will normally use 122.950 MHz.

6. What does "ATIS" mean? (AIM 4-1-13)

Automatic Terminal Information Service (ATIS) is the continuous broadcast of recorded noncontrol information in selected high-activity terminal areas. Its purpose is to improve controller effectiveness and to relieve frequency congestion by automating the repetitive transmission of essential but routine information.

7. If operating into an airport without an operating control tower, FSS or UNICOM, what procedure should be followed? (AC 61-23C)

A pilot should monitor the "MULTICOM" frequency of 122.9 when approaching the airport and broadcast intentions when approximately five miles out. MULTICOM is a mobile service not open to public use, used to provide communications essential to conduct the activities being performed by or directed from private aircraft.

8. What frequencies are monitored by most FSS's other than 121.5? (AIM 4-2-14)

FSS's and supplemental weather service locations are allocated frequencies for different functions; for example, 122.0 MHz is assigned as the Enroute Flight Advisory Service frequency at selected FSS's. In addition, certain FSS's provide Local Airport Advisory on 123.6 MHz. Frequencies are listed in the Airport/Facility Directory. If you are in doubt as to what frequency to use, 122.2 MHz is assigned to the majority of FSS's as a common enroute simplex frequency.

9. What is "Local Airport Advisory Service"? (AIM 4-1-9)

Certain FSS's provide Local Airport Advisory service to pilots when an FSS is physically located on an airport which does not have a control tower or where the tower is operated on a part-time basis. The CTAF (usually 123.6) for FSS's which provide this service will be disseminated in appropriate aeronautical publications. A CTAF FSS provides wind direction and velocity, favored or designated runway, altimeter setting, known traffic, notices to airmen, airport taxi routes, airport traffic pattern information, and instrument approach procedures. The information is advisory in nature and does not constitute an ATC clearance.

10. How can a pilot determine what frequency is appropriate for activating their VFR flight plan once airborne?

Two ways:

a. Ask the FSS briefer during the preflight weather briefing.

b. Consult the communications section under flight service for the airport of departure in the Airport/Facility Directory.

11. What is the meaning of a heavy-lined blue box surrounding a NAVAID frequency? (Chart Legend)

A heavy-lined blue box surrounding the radio station data indicates that both standard FSS frequencies are available at all altitudes without terrain interference. The standard frequencies are 121.5 and 122.2.

12. Why would a frequency be printed on top of a heavy-lined box? (Chart Legend)

This usually means that this frequency is available in addition to the standard FSS frequencies.

13. What is the meaning of a thin-lined blue box surrounding a NAVAID frequency? (Chart Legend)

A plain box without frequencies on top indicates that there are no standard FSS frequencies available. These NAVAIDs will have a "no voice" symbol (underline under frequency).

14. Why would a frequency be printed on top of a thin-lined blue box? (Chart Legend)

These frequencies are the best frequencies to use in the immediate vicinity of the NAVAID site, and will assure reception by the controlling FSS at low altitudes without terrain interference. They will normally be followed by an "R" which indicates that the FSS

Continued

can receive only on that frequency (you transmit on that frequency). The pilot will listen for a response over the NAVAID frequency.

15. What meaning does a blue square appearing in the lower right hand corner of a NAVAID frequency box have? (Chart Legend)

HIWAS is available. Hazardous Inflight Weather Advisory Service is a summary of SIGMETs (WS), Convective SIGMETs (WST), urgent PIREPs (UUA), Center Weather Advisories (CWA), AIRMETs (WA), and any other weather such as isolated thunderstorms that are rapidly developing and increasing in intensity, or low ceilings and visibilities that are becoming widespread, considered significant, and are not included in a current hazardous weather advisory.

16. What meaning does the letter "T" in a solid blue circle appearing in the top right corner of a NAVAID frequency box have? (Chart Legend)

A Transcribed Weather Broadcast is available. A TWEB is a continuous recording of meteorological and aeronautical information that is broadcast on L/MF and VOR facilities for pilots.

D. Federal Aviation Regulations Part 91

1. If an in-flight emergency requires immediate action by the pilot, what authority and responsibilities does he/she have? (14 CFR 91.3)

a. The pilot-in-command is directly responsible for, and is the final authority as to the operation of an aircraft.

b. The pilot-in-command may deviate from any regulation in Part 91 to the extent required to meet that emergency.

c. Each pilot-in-command who deviates from a Part 91 regulation must send a written report of that deviation to the FAA, upon request.

2. What restrictions apply to pilots concerning the use of drugs and alcohol? (14 CFR 91.17)

No person may act or attempt to act as a crewmember of a civil aircraft:

a. within 8 hours after the consumption of any alcoholic beverage;

b. while under the influence of alcohol;

c. while using any drug that affects the person's faculties in any way contrary to safety; or

d. while having .04 percent by weight or more alcohol in the blood.

3. Is it permissible for a pilot to allow a person who is obviously under the influence of intoxicating liquors or drugs to be carried aboard an aircraft? (14 CFR 91.17)

No. Except in an emergency, no pilot of a civil aircraft may allow a person who appears to be intoxicated or who demonstrates by manner or physical indications that the individual is under the influence of drugs (except a medical patient under proper care) to be carried in that aircraft.

4. May portable electronic devices be operated onboard an aircraft? (14 CFR 91.21)

Aircraft operated by a holder of an air carrier operating certificate or an aircraft operating under IFR may not allow operation of electronic devices onboard their aircraft. Exceptions are: portable voice recorders, hearing aids, heart pacemakers, electric shavers, or any other device that the operator of the aircraft has determined will not cause interference with the navigation or communication system of the aircraft on which it is to be used.

5. Under what conditions may objects be dropped from an aircraft? (14 CFR 91.15)

No pilot-in-command of a civil aircraft may allow any object to be dropped from that aircraft in flight that creates a hazard to persons or property. However, this section does not prohibit the dropping of any object if reasonable precautions are taken to avoid injury or damage to persons or property.

6. Concerning a flight in the local area, is any preflight action required, and if so, what must it consist of? (14 CFR 91.103)

Yes, pilots must familiarize themselves with all available information concerning that flight, including runway lengths at airports of intended use, and takeoff and landing distance data under existing conditions.

7. Preflight action as required by regulation for all flights away from the vicinity of the departure airport shall include a review of what specific information? (14 CFR 91.103)

For a flight under IFR or a flight not in the vicinity of an airport:

a. Weather reports and forecasts

b. Fuel requirements

c. Alternatives available if the planned flight cannot be completed

d. Any known traffic delays of which the pilot-in-command has been advised by ATC

e. Runway lengths of intended use

f. Takeoff and landing distance data

8. Which persons on board an aircraft are required to use seatbelts and when? (14 CFR 91.107)

Each person on board a U.S.-registered civil aircraft must occupy an approved seat or berth with a safety belt, and if installed, shoulder harness, properly secured about him or her during movement on the surface, takeoff and landing. However a person who has not reached his or her second birthday and does not occupy or use any restraining device may be held by an adult who is occupying a seat or berth, and a person on board for the purpose of engaging in sport parachuting may use the floor of the aircraft as a seat.

9. What responsibility does the pilot-in-command have concerning passengers and their use of seatbelts? (14 CFR 91.107)

No pilot may take off a U.S. registered civil aircraft unless the pilot-in-command of that aircraft ensures that each person on board is briefed on how to fasten and unfasten that person's safety belt and shoulder harness, if installed. The pilot-in-command shall ensure that all persons on board have been notified to fasten their safety belt and shoulder harness, if installed, before takeoff or landing.

10. When are flight crewmembers required to keep their seatbelts and shoulder harnesses fastened? (14 CFR 91.105)

During takeoff and landing, and while en route, each required flight crewmember shall keep his/her seatbelt fastened while at his/her station. During takeoff and landing this includes shoulder harnesses, if installed, unless it interferes with other required duties.

11. If operating an aircraft in close proximity to another, such as formation flight, what regulations apply? (14 CFR 91.111)

a. No person may operate an aircraft so close to another aircraft as to create a collision hazard.

b. No person may operate an aircraft in formation flight except by arrangement with the pilot-in-command of each aircraft in the formation.

c. No person may operate an aircraft, carrying passengers for hire, in formation flight.

12. What is the order of right-of-way as applied to the different categories of aircraft? (14 CFR 91.113)

B alloons

G liders

A irships

A irplanes

R otorcraft

Aircraft towing or refueling other aircraft have the right-of-way over all other engine-driven aircraft.

Remember: BGAAR (BIG "R")

13. When would an aircraft have the right-of-way over all other air traffic? (14 CFR 91.113)

An aircraft in distress has the right-of-way over all other air traffic.

14. State the required action for each of the aircraft confrontations (same category), below. (14 CFR 91.103)

Converging
Approaching head-on
Overtaking

Converging: aircraft on right has the right-of-way.

Approaching head-on: both aircraft shall alter course to right.

Overtaking: aircraft being overtaken has the right-of-way; pilot of the overtaking aircraft shall alter course to the right.

15. What right-of-way rules apply when two or more aircraft are approaching an airport for the purpose of landing? (14 CFR 91.113)

Aircraft on final approach to land or while landing have the right-of-way over aircraft in flight or operating on the surface, except that they shall not take advantage of this rule to force an aircraft off the runway surface which has already landed and is attempting to make way for an aircraft on final approach. When two or more aircraft are approaching an airport for the purpose of landing, the aircraft at the lower altitude has the right-of-way, but it shall not take advantage of this rule to cut in front of another which is on final approach to land or to overtake that aircraft.

16. Unless otherwise authorized or required by ATC, what is the maximum indicated airspeed at which a person may operate an aircraft below 10,000 feet MSL? (14 CFR 91.117)

No person may operate an aircraft below 10,000 feet MSL at an indicated airspeed of more than 250 knots (288 MPH).

17. What is the minimum safe altitude that an aircraft may be operated over a congested area of a city? (14 CFR 91.119)

Except when necessary for takeoff or landing, no person may operate an aircraft over a congested area of a city, town, or settlement, or over any open-air assembly of persons, below an altitude of 1,000 feet above the highest obstacle within a horizontal radius of 2,000 feet of the aircraft.

18. In areas other than congested areas, what minimum safe altitudes shall be used? (14 CFR 91.119)

Except when necessary for takeoff or landing, an aircraft shall be operated no lower than 500 feet above the surface, except over open water or sparsely populated areas. In those cases, the aircraft may not be operated closer than 500 feet to any person, vessel, vehicle or structure.

19. Define "minimum safe altitude." (14 CFR 91.119)

An altitude allowing, if a power unit fails, an emergency landing without undue hazard to persons or property on the surface.

20. What is the lowest altitude an aircraft may be operated over an area designated as a U.S. Wildlife refuge, park or Forest Service Area? (AIM 7-4-6)

All aircraft are requested to maintain a minimum altitude of 2,000 feet above the surface.

21. When flying below 18,000 feet MSL, cruising altitude must be maintained by reference to an altimeter set using what procedure? (14 CFR 91.121)

When the barometric pressure is 31.00" Hg or less, each person operating an aircraft shall maintain the cruising altitude or flight level of that aircraft, as the case may be, by reference to an altimeter set to the current reported altimeter setting of a station along the route and within 100 nautical miles of the aircraft. If there is no station within this area, the current reported altimeter setting of an available station may be used. If the barometric pressure exceeds 31.00" Hg, consult the *Aeronautical Information Manual* for correct procedures.

22. If an altimeter setting is not available before flight, what procedure should be used? (14 CFR 91.121)

Use the same procedure as in the case of an aircraft not equipped with a radio: the elevation of the departure airport or an appropriate altimeter setting available before departure should be used.

23. Concerning ATC clearances and instructions, what is the one exception to the regulation that states that no pilot may deviate from an ATC clearance unless an amended clearance has been received? (14 CFR 91.123)

When an ATC clearance has been obtained, no pilot-in-command may deviate from that clearance, except in an emergency, unless an amended clearance has been obtained.

24. As pilot-in-command, what action, if any, is required of you if you deviate from an ATC instruction and priority is given? (14 CFR 91.123)

Two actions are required of you as PIC:

a. Each pilot-in-command who, in an emergency, deviates from an ATC clearance or instruction shall notify ATC of that deviation as soon as possible (in-the-air responsibility).

b. Each pilot-in-command who is given priority by ATC in an emergency shall submit a detailed report of that emergency within 48 hours to the manager of that ATC facility, if requested by ATC (on-the-ground responsibility).

25. In the event of radio failure while operating an aircraft to, from, through or on an airport having an operational tower, what are the different types and meanings of light gun signals you might receive from an ATC tower? (14 CFR 91.125)

Light	On Ground	In Air
Steady Green	Cleared for Takeoff	Cleared to Land
Flashing Green	Cleared to Taxi	Return for Landing
Steady Red	Stop	Yield, Continue Circling
Flashing Red	Taxi Clear of Runway	Unsafe, Do Not Land
Flashing White	Return to Start	Not Used
Alternate Red/ Green	Exercise Extreme Caution	Exercise Extreme Caution

Note: Most pilots find these hard to remember; attach them to your kneeboard or your flight log form.

26. **If the aircraft radio fails in flight under VFR while operating into a tower controlled airport, what conditions must be met before a landing may be made at that airport?** (14 CFR 91.126, 91.127, 91.129)

   a. Weather conditions must be at or above basic VFR weather minimums,

   b. Visual contact with the tower is maintained; and

   c. A clearance to land is received.

27. **What procedures should be used when attempting communications with a tower when the aircraft transmitter or receiver or both are inoperative?** (AIM 4-2-13)

   Arriving Aircraft Receiver Inoperative:

   a. Remain outside or above Class D surface area.

   b. Determine direction and flow of traffic.

   c. Advise tower of aircraft type, position, altitude and intention to land.

   d. At 3 to 5 miles, advise tower of position and join traffic pattern.

   e. Watch tower for light gun signals.

   Arriving Aircraft Transmitter Inoperative:

   a. Remain outside or above Class D surface area.

   b. Determine direction and flow of traffic.

   c. Monitor frequency for landing or traffic information.

   d. Join the traffic pattern and watch for light gun signals.

   e. Daytime, acknowledge by rocking wings. Nighttime, acknowledge by flashing landing light or navigation lights.

   Arriving Aircraft Transmitter and Receiver Inoperative:

   a. Remain outside or above Class D surface area.

   b. Determine direction and flow of traffic.

   c. Join the traffic pattern and watch for light gun signals.

   d. Acknowledge light signals as noted above.

28. What general rules apply concerning traffic pattern operations at non-tower airports within Class E or G airspace? (14 CFR 91.126, 91.127)

Each person operating an aircraft to or from an airport without an operating control tower shall:

a. in the case of an airplane approaching to land, make all turns of that airplane to the left unless the airport displays approved light signals or visual markings indicating that turns should be made to the right, in which case the pilot shall make all turns to the right.

b. in the case of an aircraft departing an airport, comply with any traffic patterns established for that airport in Part 93.

29. What procedure should be used when approaching to land on a runway with a Visual Approach Slope Indicator? (14 CFR 91.129)

Aircraft approaching to land on a runway served by a Visual Approach Slope Indicator shall maintain an altitude at or above the glide slope until a lower altitude is necessary for a safe landing.

30. What is the fuel requirement for VFR flight at night? (14 CFR 91.151)

No person may begin a flight in an airplane under VFR conditions unless (considering wind and forecast weather conditions) there is enough fuel to fly to the first point of intended landing and, assuming normal cruising speed, at night, to fly after that for at least 45 minutes.

31. What is the fuel requirement for VFR flight during the day? (14 CFR 91.151)

During the day, you must be able to fly to the first point of intended landing, and assuming normal cruising speed, to fly after that for at least 30 minutes.

32. When operating an aircraft under VFR in level cruising flight at an altitude of more than 3,000 feet above the surface, what rules apply concerning specific altitudes flown? (14 CFR 91.159)

When operating above 3,000 feet AGL but less than 18,000 feet MSL on a *magnetic course* of 0° to 179°, fly at an odd thousand foot MSL altitude plus 500 feet. When on a *magnetic course* of 180° to 359°, fly at an even-thousand-foot MSL altitude plus 500 feet.

33. What instruments and equipment are required for VFR day flight? (14 CFR 91.205)

For VFR flight during the day, the following instruments and equipment are required:

a. Airspeed indicator

b. Altimeter

c. Magnetic direction indicator compass

d. Tachometer for each engine

e. Oil pressure gauge for each engine

f. Temperature gauge for each liquid-cooled engine

g. Oil temperature gauge for each air-cooled engine

h. Manifold pressure gauge for each altitude engine

i. Fuel gauge indicating the quantity in each tank

j. Landing gear position indicator

k. For small civil airplanes certificated after March 11, 1996, an approved aviation red or aviation white anticollision light system.

l. Flotation gear (if operated for hire over water beyond power-off gliding distance from shore)

m. Safety belts (approved metal-to-metal latching device for each occupant over 2 years old)

n. Shoulder harnesses (for each front seat if aircraft manufactured after 1978)

o. Emergency locator transmitter (if required by 14 CFR 91.207)

34. What instruments and equipment are required for VFR night flight? (14 CFR 91.205)

For VFR flight at night, the following instruments and equipment are required:

a. Instruments and equipment required for VFR day flight;

b. Approved position lights (navigation lights);

c. An approved aviation red or aviation white anticollision light system;

d. If the aircraft is operated for hire, one electric landing light;

e. An adequate source of electrical energy for all installed electrical and radio equipment; and

f. One spare set of fuses, or three spare fuses of each kind required, that are accessible to the pilot in flight.

35. What is an "ELT"? (AIM Glossary)

Emergency Locator Transmitter—A radio transmitter attached to the aircraft structure which operates from its own power source on 121.5 and 243.0 MHz. It aids in locating downed aircraft by radiating a downward-seeping audio tone, 2-4 times a second. It is designed to function without human action after an accident. It can be operationally tested during the first 5 minutes after any hour.

36. Is an emergency locator transmitter required on all aircraft? (14 CFR 91.207)

No person may operate a U.S. registered civil airplane unless there is attached to the airplane an automatic-type emergency locator transmitter that is in operable condition. Several exceptions exist, including the following:

a. Aircraft engaged in training operations conducted entirely within a 50-nautical-mile radius of the airport from which such local flight operations began.

b. Aircraft engaged in design and testing.

c. New aircraft engaged in manufacture, preparation and delivery.

d. Aircraft engaged in agricultural operations.

37. When must the batteries in an emergency locator transmitter be replaced or recharged, if rechargeable?
(14 CFR 91.207)

Batteries used in ELTs must be replaced (or recharged, if the batteries are rechargeable):

a. When the transmitter has been in use for more than 1 cumulative hour; or

b. When 50 percent of their useful life (or, if rechargeable batteries, 50 percent of their useful life of charge), has expired.

38. What are the regulations concerning use of supplemental oxygen onboard an aircraft? (14 CFR 91.211)

a. At cabin pressure altitudes above 12,500 feet MSL up to and including 14,000 feet MSL: for that part of the flight at those altitudes that is more than 30 minutes, the required minimum flight crew must be provided with and use supplemental oxygen.

b. At cabin pressure altitudes above 14,000 feet MSL: for the entire flight time at those altitudes, the required flight crew is provided with and uses supplemental oxygen.

c. At cabin pressure altitudes above 15,000 feet MSL: each occupant is provided with supplemental oxygen.

39. According to regulations, where is aerobatic flight of an aircraft not permitted? (14 CFR 91.303)

No person may operate an aircraft in aerobatic flight:

a. Over any congested area of a city, town, or settlement;

b. Over an open air assembly of persons;

c. Within the lateral boundaries of the surface areas of Class B, Class C, Class D, or Class E airspace designated for an airport;

d. Within 4 nautical miles of the center line of a Federal airway;

e. Below an altitude of 1,500 feet above the surface; or

f. When flight visibility is less than 3 statute miles.

40. Define aerobatic flight. (14 CFR 91.303)

For the purposes of this section, aerobatic flight means an intentional maneuver involving an abrupt change in an aircraft's attitude, an abnormal attitude, or abnormal acceleration, not necessary for normal flight.

41. When are parachutes required onboard an aircraft? (14 CFR 91.307)

a. Unless each occupant of the aircraft is wearing an approved parachute, no pilot of a civil aircraft carrying any person (other than a crewmember) may execute any intentional maneuver that exceeds:

    i. a bank angle of 60° relative to the horizon; or

    ii. a nose-up or nose-down attitude of 30° relative to the horizon.

b. The above regulation does not apply to:

    i. flight tests for pilot certification or rating; or

    ii. spins and other flight maneuvers required by the regulations for any certificate or rating when given by a CFI or ATP instructing in accordance with 14 CFR 61.169.

E. Airspace

1. What is Class A airspace? (AIM 3-2-2)

Generally, that airspace from 18,000 feet MSL up to and including FL600, including that airspace overlying the waters within 12 nautical miles of the coast of the 48 contiguous states and Alaska; and designated international airspace beyond 12 nautical miles of the coast of the 48 contiguous states and Alaska within areas of domestic radio navigational signal or ATC radar coverage, and within which domestic procedures are applied.

2. Can a flight under VFR be conducted within Class A airspace? (14 CFR 91.135)

No, unless otherwise authorized by ATC, each person operating an aircraft in Class A airspace must operate that aircraft under instrument flight rules (IFR).

3. What is the minimum pilot certification for operations conducted within Class A airspace? (14 CFR 91.135)

The pilot must be at least a private pilot with an instrument rating.

4. What minimum equipment is required for flight operations within Class A airspace? (14 CFR 91.135)

a. A two-way radio capable of communicating with ATC on the frequency assigned.

b. A Mode C altitude encoding transponder.

c. Equipped with instruments and equipment required for IFR operations.

5. How is Class A airspace depicted on navigational charts? (AIM 3-2-2)

Class A airspace is not specifically charted.

6. What is the definition of Class B airspace? (AIM 3-2-3)

Generally, that airspace from the surface to 10,000 feet MSL surrounding the nation's busiest airports in terms of IFR operations or passenger enplanements. The configuration of each Class B airspace area is individually tailored and consists of a surface area and two or more layers (some Class B airspace areas resemble upside down wedding cakes), and is designated to contain all published instrument procedures once an aircraft enters the airspace.

7. What minimum pilot certification is required to operate an aircraft within Class B airspace? (14 CFR 91.131)

No person may takeoff or land a civil aircraft at an airport within a Class B airspace, including the primary airport, or operate a civil aircraft within a Class B airspace area unless that person holds at least a private pilot certificate or is a student or recreational pilot who has met the requirements of 14 CFR 61.95.

Certain Class B airspace areas do not allow pilot operations to be conducted to or from the primary airport, unless the pilot-in-command holds at least a private pilot certificate (example: Dallas/Fort Worth International).

8. What is the minimum equipment required for operations of an aircraft within Class B airspace? (14 CFR 91.131)

a. An operable two-way radio capable of communications with ATC on the appropriate frequencies for that area.

b. A Mode C altitude encoding transponder.

c. If IFR, a VOR receiver is also required.

9. Before operating an aircraft into Class B airspace, what basic requirement must be met? (14 CFR 91.131)

Arriving aircraft must obtain an ATC clearance from the ATC facility having jurisdiction for that area prior to operating an aircraft in that area.

10. What minimum weather conditions are required when conducting VFR flight operations within Class B airspace? (14 CFR 91.155)

VFR flight operations must be conducted clear of clouds with at least 3 statute miles flight visibility.

11. How is Class B (TCA) airspace depicted on navigational charts? (AIM 3-2-3)

Class B airspace is charted on Sectional Charts, IFR En Route Low Altitude, and Terminal Area Charts. A solid shaded blue line depicts the lateral limits of Class B airspace. Numbers indicate the base and top, i.e. $^{100}/_{25}$, $^{100}/_{SFC}$.

12. What basic ATC services are provided to all aircraft operating within Class B airspace? (AIM 3-2-3)

VFR pilots will be provided sequencing and separation from other aircraft while operating within Class B airspace.

13. It becomes apparent that wake turbulence may be encountered while ATC is providing sequencing and separation services in Class B airspace. Whose responsibility is it to avoid this turbulence? (AIM 3-2-3)

The pilot-in-command is responsible. The services provided by ATC do not relieve pilots of their responsibilities to see and avoid other traffic operating in basic VFR weather conditions, to adjust their operations and flight path as necessary to preclude serious wake turbulence encounters, to maintain appropriate terrain and obstruction clearance, or to remain in weather conditions equal to or better than the minimums required by 14 CFR 91.155.

14. What is the maximum speed allowed when operating inside Class B airspace, under 10,000 feet and within a Class D surface area? (14 CFR 91.117)

Unless otherwise authorized or required by ATC, no person may operate an aircraft at or below 2,500 feet above the surface within 4 nautical miles of the primary airport of a Class C or Class D airspace area at an indicated airspeed of more than 200 knots. This restriction does not apply to operations conducted within a Class B airspace area. Such operations shall comply with the "below 10,000 feet MSL" restriction: "No person shall operate an aircraft below 10,000 feet MSL, at an indicated airspeed of more than 250 knots."

15. When operating beneath the lateral limits of Class B airspace, or in a VFR corridor designated through Class B airspace, what maximum speed is authorized? (14 CFR 91.117)

No person may operate an aircraft in the airspace underlying a Class B airspace area designated for an airport or in a VFR corridor designated through such a Class B airspace area, at an indicated airspeed of more than 200 knots (230 mph).

16. What is Class C airspace? (AIM 3-2-4)

Generally, that airspace from the surface to 4,000 feet above the airport elevation (charted in MSL) surrounding those airports that have an operational control tower, are serviced by a radar approach control, and that have a certain number of IFR operations or passenger enplanements.

17. What are the basic dimensions of Class C airspace? (AIM 3-2-4)

Although the configuration of each Class C airspace area is individually tailored, the airspace usually consists of two circles both centered on the primary airport for the Class C airspace. The inner circle has a radius of 5 NM. The outer circle has a radius of 10 NM. The airspace of the inner circle extends from the surface up to 4,000 feet above the airport. The airspace area between the 5 and 10 NM rings begin at a height 1,200 feet AGL and extends to the same altitude cap as the inner circle. The outer area consists of airspace beginning at 10 NM extending to a radius of 20 NM from the primary airport and extends from the lower limits of radar/radio coverage up to the ceiling of the approach controls delegated airspace.

18. What minimum pilot certification is required to operate an aircraft within Class C airspace? (AIM 3-2-4)

A student pilot certificate.

19. What minimum equipment is required to operate an aircraft within Class C airspace? (14 CFR 91.130, 91.215)

Unless otherwise authorized by the ATC having jurisdiction over the Class C airspace area, no person may operate an aircraft within a Class C airspace area designated for an airport unless that aircraft is equipped with the following:

a. A two-way radio.

b. Automatic pressure altitude reporting equipment having Mode C capability.

20. When operating an aircraft through Class C airspace or to an airport within Class C airspace, what basic requirement must be met? (14 CFR 91.130)

Each person must establish two-way radio communications with the ATC facilities providing air traffic services prior to entering that airspace and thereafter maintain those communications while within that airspace.

21. Two-way radio communications must be established prior to entering Class C airspace. Define what is meant by "established" in this context. (AIM 3-2-4)

If a controller responds to a radio call with, "(aircraft call sign) standby," radio communications have been established. It is important to understand that if the controller responds to the initial radio call *without* using the aircraft identification, radio communications have *not* been established and the pilot may not enter the Class C airspace.

22. When departing a satellite airport without an operative control tower located within Class C airspace, what requirement must be met? (14 CFR 91.130)

Each person must establish and maintain two-way radio communications with the ATC facilities having jurisdiction over the Class C airspace area as soon as practicable after departing.

23. What minimum weather conditions are required when conducting VFR flight operations within Class C airspace? (14 CFR 91.155)

VFR flight operations within Class C airspace require 3 statute miles flight visibility and cloud clearances of at least 500 feet below, 1,000 feet above and 2,000 feet horizontal to clouds.

24. How is Class C airspace depicted on navigational charts? (AIM 3-2-4)

A solid magenta line is used to depict Class C airspace. Class C airspace is charted on Sectional Charts, IFR En Route Low Altitude, and Terminal Area Charts where appropriate.

25. What type of Air Traffic Control services are provided when operating within Class C airspace? (AIM 3-2-4)

When two-way radio communications and radar contact are established, all participating VFR aircraft are:

a. Sequenced to the primary airport.

b. Provided Class C services within the Class C airspace and the outer area.

c. Provided basic radar services beyond the outer area on a workload permitting basis. This can be terminated by the controller if workload dictates.

26. Describe the various types of terminal radar services available for VFR aircraft. (AIM 4-1-17)

Basic radar service — Safety alerts, traffic advisories, limited radar vectoring (on a workload-permitting basis) and sequencing at locations where procedures have been established for this purpose and/or when covered by a letter of agreement.

TRSA service — radar sequencing and separation service for VFR aircraft in a TRSA.

Class C service — This service provides, in addition to basic radar service, approved separation between IFR, and VFR aircraft, and sequencing of VFR arrivals to the primary airport.

Continued

Class B service — Provides, in addition to basic radar service, approved separation of aircraft based on IFR, VFR, and/or weight, and sequencing of VFR arrivals to the primary airport(s).

27. Where is Mode C altitude encoding transponder equipment required? (14 CFR 91.215)

a. In Class A, Class B, and Class C airspace areas.

b. In all airspace within a 30 mile radius of the primary airport for which a Class B airspace area has been designated, from the surface to 10,000 feet MSL.

c. In all airspace above the ceiling and within the lateral boundaries of a Class B or Class C airspace area designated for an airport upward to 10,000 feet MSL.

d. In all airspace of the 48 contiguous states and the district of Columbia at and above 10,000 feet MSL, excluding the airspace at and below 2,500 feet above the surface.

e. In the airspace from the surface to 10,000 feet MSL within a 10 nautical mile radius of designated airports, excluding that airspace below 1,200 feet AGL outside of the lateral boundaries.

28. What is the maximum speed an aircraft may be operated within Class C airspace? (AIM 3-2-4)

Unless otherwise authorized or required by ATC, no person may operate an aircraft at or below 2,500 feet above the surface within 4 nautical miles of the primary airport of a Class C airspace area at an indicated speed of more than 200 knots (230 mph).

29. What is Class D airspace? (AIM 3-2-5)

Generally, that airspace from the surface to 2,500 feet above the airport elevation (charted in MSL) surrounding those airports that have an operational control tower. The configuration of each Class D airspace area is individually tailored and when instrument procedures are published, the airspace will normally be designed to contain those procedures.

30. When operating an aircraft through Class D airspace or to an airport within Class D airspace, what requirement must be met? (14 CFR 91.129)

Each person must establish two-way radio communications with the ATC facilities providing air traffic services prior to entering that airspace and thereafter maintain those communications while within that airspace.

31. When departing a satellite airport without an operative control tower located within Class D airspace, what requirement must be met? (14 CFR 91.129)

Each person must establish and maintain two-way radio communications with the ATC facility having jurisdiction over the Class D airspace area as soon as practicable after departing.

32. Is an ATC clearance required, if flight operations are conducted through a Class D arrival extension area? (AIM 3-2-6)

Arrival extensions for instrument approach procedures may be Class D or Class E airspace. Arrival extensions will either be charted as part of the basic surface area with the blue segmented line indicating Class D airspace or as a separate surface area indicated by the magenta segmented line (Class E airspace). Communications with Air Traffic Control is recommended but is not required of aircraft operating under VFR within the airspace encompassed by the magenta lines, indicating Class E airspace.

33. What minimum weather conditions are required when conducting VFR flight operations within Class D airspace? (14 CFR 91.155)

VFR flight operations within Class D airspace require 3 statute miles flight visibility and cloud clearances of at least 500 feet below, 1,000 feet above and 2,000 feet horizontal to clouds.

34. How is Class D airspace depicted on navigational charts? (AIM 3-2-5)

Class D airspace areas are depicted on Sectional and Terminal charts with blue segmented lines, and on IFR Low Altitude charts with a boxed [D]. Arrival extensions will be charted as part of the basic surface area with blue segmented symbology or as a separate surface area indicated by the magenta segmented line. Communications with Air Traffic Control is recommended but is not required of aircraft operating under VFR within the airspace encompassed by the magenta lines which will be Class E airspace.

35. What type of Air Traffic Control services are provided when operating within Class D airspace? (AIM 3-2-5, 5-5-8, 5-5-10)

No separation services are provided to VFR aircraft. When meteorological conditions permit, regardless of the type of flight plan or whether or not under the control of a radar facility, the pilot is responsible to see and avoid other traffic, terrain or obstacles. A controller, on a workload permitting basis, will provide radar traffic information, safety alerts and traffic information for sequencing purposes.

36. What is the maximum speed an aircraft may be operated within Class D airspace? (AIM 3-2-5)

Unless otherwise authorized or required by ATC, no person may operate an aircraft at or below 2,500 feet above the surface within 4 nautical miles of the primary airport of a Class D airspace area at an indicated airspeed of more than 200 knots (230 mph).

37. When a control tower, located at an airport within Class D airspace, ceases operation for the day, what happens to the lower limit of the controlled airspace? (AIM 3-2-5)

During the hours the tower is not in operation, Class E surface area rules, or a combination of Class E rules down to 700 feet AGL and Class G rules to the surface, will become applicable. Check the A/FD for specifics.

38. Will all airports with an operating control tower always have Class D airspace surrounding them?

No; some airports do not have the required weather reporting capability necessary for surface based controlled airspace. The controlled airspace over these airports normally begins at 700 feet or 1,200 feet AGL and can be determined from visual aeronautical charts.

39. What is the definition of Class E (controlled) airspace? (AIM 3-2-6)

Generally, if the airspace is not Class A, Class B, Class C, or Class D, and it is controlled airspace, it is Class E airspace.

40. State several examples of Class E airspace. (AIM 3-2-6)

a. A surface area designated for an airport and configured to contain all instrument approaches.

b. An extension to a surface area — There are Class E airspace areas that serve as extensions to Class B, Class C, and Class D surface areas designated for an airport. Such airspace provides controlled airspace to contain standard instrument approach procedures without imposing a communications requirement on pilots operating under VFR.

c. Airspace used for transition — Class E airspace beginning at either 700 or 1,200 feet AGL used to transition to/from the terminal enroute environment.

d. En Route Domestic Areas — Class E airspace areas that extend upward from a specified altitude and provide controlled airspace in those areas where there is a requirement to provide IFR en route ATC services but the Federal airway system is inadequate.

e. Federal Airways — The federal airways are within Class E airspace areas and, unless otherwise specified, extend upward from 1,200 feet to, but not including 18,000 feet MSL.

Continued

f. Offshore Airspace areas—Class E airspace that extend upward from a specified altitude to, but not including 18,000 feet MSL. These areas provide controlled airspace beyond 12 miles from the coast of the United States in those areas where there is a requirement to provide IFR en route ATC services.

g. Unless designated at a lower altitude—Class E airspace begins at 14,500 feet MSL to, but not including 18,000 feet MSL overlying the 48 contiguous states, including the waters within 12 miles from the coast of the 48 contiguous states; the District of Columbia; Alaska, including the waters within 12 miles from the coast of Alaska, and airspace above FL600, excluding specified areas in Alaska.

41. What are the operating rules and pilot/equipment requirements to operate within Class E airspace? (AIM 3-2-6)

a. Minimum pilot certification—student pilot certificate.

b. No specific equipment requirements in Class E airspace.

c. No specific requirements for arrival or through flight in Class E airspace.

42. What basic operational requirement must be met if flight operations are to be conducted into a Class E surface area located at a non-tower airport with a prescribed instrument approach? (AIM 3-2-6)

As long as the weather allows flight operations to be conducted under basic VFR minimums, a flight into or out of the Class E airspace may be made without an ATC clearance. However, if basic VFR minimums cannot be maintained an ATC clearance will be necessary for arrival or departure (Special VFR clearance).

43. Are you required to establish communications with a tower located within Class E airspace? (14 CFR 91.127)

Yes; unless otherwise authorized or required by ATC, no person may operate an aircraft to, from, through, or on an airport having an operational control tower unless two-way communications are maintained between that aircraft and the control tower. Communications must be established prior to 4 nautical miles from the airport, up to and including 2,500 feet AGL.

44. How is Class E airspace depicted on navigational charts? (AIM 3-2-6)

Class E airspace below 14,500 feet MSL is charted on Sectional, Terminal, World, and IFR Enroute Low Altitude Charts. Class E airspace without an operating control tower but with prescribed instrument approaches is depicted with a magenta segmented line which denotes controlled airspace extending upward from the surface to the overlying or floor of the adjacent controlled airspace. Vertical limits are not depicted. The light blue shaded line is no longer used to depict the 1,200 foot or above Class E airspace (transition area), unless it abuts uncontrolled airspace. Where the outer edge of the 700 foot Class E airspace (transition area, magenta shaded line) ends, the 1,200 foot or greater area automatically begins.

45. What is the definition of Class G airspace? (AIM 3-3-1)

Class G or uncontrolled airspace is that portion of the airspace that has not been designated as Class A, B, C, D and E airspace.

46. Are you required to establish communications with a tower located within Class G airspace? (14 CFR 91.126)

Yes; unless otherwise authorized or required by ATC, no person may operate an aircraft to, from, through, or on an airport having an operational control tower unless two-way communications are maintained between that aircraft and the control tower. Communications must be established prior to 4 nautical miles from the airport, up to and including 2,500 AGL.

47. What are the vertical limits of Class G airspace?

Class G airspace begins at the surface and continues up to but not including the overlying controlled airspace or 14,500 MSL, where Class E airspace begins, whichever occurs first.

48. What is the minimum cloud clearance and visibility required when conducting flight operations in a traffic pattern at night in Class G airspace? (14 CFR 91.155)

When the visibility is less than 3 statute miles but not less than 1 statute mile during night hours, an airplane may be operated clear of clouds if operated in an airport traffic pattern within one half mile of the runway.

49. What is the main difference between Class G airspace and Class A, B, C, D, E airspace?

The main difference which distinguishes Class G airspace from Class A, B, C, D, and E airspace is the flight visibility/cloud clearance requirements necessary to operate within it.

50. What minimum flight visibility and clearance from clouds are required for VFR flight in the following situations? (14 CFR 91.155)

CLASS C, D, or E AIRSPACE

Less than 10,000 feet MSL:
Visibility: 3 statute miles.
Cloud clearance: 500 feet below, 1,000 feet above, 2,000 feet horizontal.

At or above 10,000 feet MSL:
Visibility: 5 statute miles.
Cloud clearance: 1,000 feet below, 1,000 feet above, 1 statute mile horizontal.

CLASS G AIRSPACE

1,200 feet or less above the surface (regardless of MSL altitude):
DAY:
Visibility: 1 statute mile.
Cloud clearance: clear of clouds
NIGHT:
Visibility: 3 statute miles
Cloud clearance: 500 feet below, 1,000 feet above, 2,000 feet horizontal.

More than 1,200 ft. above the surface but less than 10,000 ft. MSL:
DAY:
Visibility: 1 statute mile
Cloud clearance: 500 feet below, 1,000 feet above, 2,000 feet horizontal.
NIGHT:
Visibility: 3 statute miles
Cloud clearance: 500 feet below, 1,000 feet above, 2,000 feet horizontal.

More than 1,200 ft. above the surface and at or above 10,000 ft. MSL:
Visibility: 5 statute miles
Cloud clearance: 1,000 feet below, 1,000 feet above, 1 statute mile horizontal.

51. **What are the "basic" VFR weather minimums required for operation of an aircraft into Class B, Class C, Class D, or Class E airspace?** (14 CFR 91.155)

No person may operate an aircraft, under VFR, within the lateral boundaries of the surface areas of Class C, Class D, or Class E airspace designated for an airport when the ceiling is less than 1,000 feet and the ground visibility is less than 3 statute miles. If ground visibility is not reported at that airport, unless flight visibility during landing or takeoff, or while operating in the traffic pattern is at least 3 statute miles. *Note:* Class B only requires clear of clouds and 3 statute miles visibility.

52. **If VFR flight minimums cannot be maintained, can a VFR flight be made into Class B, C, D, or E airspace?** (AIM 4-4-5)

No, with one exception. A "Special VFR clearance" may be obtained from the controlling authority prior to entering the Class B, C, D, or E airspace provided the flight can be made clear of clouds with at least one statute mile ground visibility if taking off or landing. If ground visibility is not reported at that airport, the flight visibility must be at least 1 statute mile.

53. Are Special VFR clearances always available to pilots in all classes of airspace? (AIM 4-4-5)

A VFR pilot may request and be given a clearance to enter, leave, or operate within most Class D and Class E surface areas and some Class B and Class C surface areas traffic permitting and providing such flight will not delay IFR operations.

Note: Special VFR operations by fixed wing aircraft are prohibited in some Class B and Class C surface areas due to the volume of IFR traffic. A list of these Class B and Class C surface areas is contained in 14 CFR Part 91. They are also depicted on Sectional Aeronautical Charts.

54. If it becomes apparent that a special VFR clearance will be necessary, what facility should the pilot contact in order to obtain one? (AIM 4-4-5)

Within Class B, C, or D airspace, requests for clearances should be made to the tower. If no tower is located within the airspace (Class E airspace), a clearance may be obtained from the nearest tower, FSS, or center.

55. Can a "Special VFR clearance" be obtained into or out of Class B, C, D, or E airspace at night? (AIM 4-4-5)

Special VFR operations by fixed-wing aircraft are prohibited between sunset and sunrise unless the pilot is instrument rated and the aircraft is equipped for IFR flight.

56. What is a "Prohibited Area"? (AIM 3-4-2)

Prohibited areas contain certain airspace of defined dimensions identified by an area on the surface of the earth within which the flight of aircraft is prohibited. Such areas are established for security or other reasons associated with the national welfare.

57. What is a "Restricted Area"? (AIM 3-4-3)

Restricted areas contain airspace identified by an area on the surface of the earth within which the flight of aircraft, while not wholly prohibited, is subject to restrictions. These areas denote the existence of unusual, often invisible, hazards to aircraft such as artillery firing, aerial gunnery, or guided missiles. Penetration of restricted areas without authorization from the using or controlling agency may be extremely hazardous to the aircraft and its occupants.

58. Under what conditions, if any, may pilots enter restricted or prohibited areas? (14 CFR 91.133)

No person may operate an aircraft within a restricted area contrary to the restrictions imposed, or within a prohibited area, unless that person has the permission of the using or controlling agency. Normally *no* operations are permitted within a prohibited area and *prior* permission must always be obtained before operating within a restricted area.

59. What is a "Warning Area"? (AIM 3-4-4)

A warning area is airspace of defined dimensions extending from three nautical miles outward from the coast of the United States, containing activity that may be hazardous to nonparticipating aircraft. The purpose of such an area is to warn nonparticipating pilots of the potential danger. A warning area may be located over domestic or international waters, or both.

60. What is a "MOA"? (AIM 3-4-5)

A Military Operating Area (MOA) consists of airspace of defined vertical and lateral limits established for the purpose of separating certain military training activities from IFR traffic. Pilots operating under VFR should exercise extreme caution while flying within an MOA when military activity is being conducted. The activity status (active/inactive) of MOAs may change frequently. Therefore, pilots should contact any FSS within 100 miles of the area to obtain accurate real-time information concerning the MOA hours of operation. Prior to entering an active MOA, pilots should contact the controlling agency for traffic advisories.

61. What is an "Alert Area"? (AIM 3-4-6)

Alert areas are depicted on aeronautical charts to inform nonparticipating pilots of areas that may contain a high volume of pilot training or an unusual type of aerial activity. Pilots should be particularly alert when flying in these areas. All activity within an Alert Area shall be conducted in accordance with regulations, without waiver, and pilots of participating aircraft as well as pilots transiting the area shall be equally responsible for collision avoidance.

62. What are "Controlled Firing Areas"? (AIM 3-4-7)

Controlled Firing Areas (CFAs) contain activities that, if not conducted in a controlled environment, could be hazardous to nonparticipating aircraft. The distinguishing feature of the CFA, as compared to other special use airspace, is that its activities are suspended immediately when spotter aircraft, radar or ground lookout positions indicate an aircraft might be approaching the area. CFAs are not charted.

63. What is a "National Security Area"? (AIM 3-4-8)

National Security Areas consist of airspace of defined vertical and lateral dimensions established at locations where there is a requirement for increased security and safety of ground facilities. Pilots are requested to voluntarily avoid flying through the depicted NSA. When is it necessary to provide a greater level of security and safety, flight in NSAs may be temporarily prohibited by regulation under the provisions of 14 CFR 99.7.

64. Where can information on special use airspace be found?

The chart legend contains information on special use airspace such as times of use, altitudes of use, and the controlling agency.

65. Where can a pilot find information on VFR flyways, VFR Corridors, Class B airspace transition routes, and Terminal Area VFR routes used to transition busy terminal airspace? (AIM 3-5-5)

Information will normally be depicted on the reverse side of VFR Terminal Area Charts, commonly referred to as Class B airspace charts.

66. What is an "Airport Advisory Area"? (AIM 3-5-1)

An airport advisory area is the area within 10 statute miles of an airport where a control tower is not operating but where a FSS is located. At such locations, the FSS provides advisory service to arriving aircraft. It is not mandatory that pilots participate in the Airport Advisory program, but it is strongly recommended they do so.

67. What are "Military Training Routes"? (AIM 3-5-2)

Military Training Routes are developed for use by the military for the purpose of conducting low-altitude, high speed training. The routes above 1,500 feet AGL are developed to be flown, to the maximum extent possible, under IFR. The routes at 1,500 feet AGL and below are generally developed to be flown under VFR. Routes below 1,500 feet AGL use four-digit identifiers (i.e. IR 1004, VR 1008). Routes above 1,500 feet AGL use three-digit identifiers, (i.e. IR 003, VR 004). IR is for IFR routes and VR is for VFR routes.

68. What is a "TRSA"? (AIM Glossary)

A Terminal Radar Service Area (TRSA) consists of airspace surrounding designated airports wherein ATC provides radar vectoring, sequencing, and separation on a full time basis for all IFR and participating VFR aircraft. Pilot participation is urged but not mandatory.

69. What class of airspace is a "TRSA"? (AIM 3-5-7)

TRSAs do not fit into any of the U.S. airspace classes and are not contained in 14 CFR Part 71 nor are there any operating rules in Part 91. The primary airport(s) within the TRSA become Class D airspace. The remaining portion of a TRSA overlies other controlled airspace which is normally Class E airspace beginning at 700 or 1,200 feet and established to transition to/from the enroute/terminal environment. TRSAs will continue to be an airspace area where participating pilots can receive additional radar services which have been redefined as TRSA service.

70. How are TRSAs depicted on navigational charts? (AIM 3-5-7)

TRSAs are depicted on visual charts with a solid black line and altitudes for each segment. The Class D portion is charted with a blue segmented line.

71. What is an "ADIZ"? (AIM 5-6-1)

All aircraft entering domestic U.S. airspace from points outside must provide for identification prior to entry. To facilitate early identification of all aircraft in the vicinity of U.S. and international airspace boundaries, Air Defense Identification Zones (ADIZ) have been established.

72. What requirements must be satisfied prior to operations into, within or across an ADIZ? (AIM 5-6-1)

Operational requirements for aircraft operations associated with an ADIZ are as follows:

Flight plan—An IFR or DVFR flight plan must be filed with the appropriate aeronautical facility.

Two-way radio—An operating two-way radio is required.

Transponder—Aircraft must be equipped with an operable radar beacon transponder having altitude reporting (Mode C) capabilities. The transponder must be turned on and set to the assigned ATC code.

Position reports—For IFR flights, normal position reporting. For DVFR flights, an estimated time of ADIZ penetration must be filed at least 15 minutes prior to entry.

Aircraft position tolerances—Over land, a tolerance of ±5 minutes from the estimated time over a reporting point and within 10 NM from the centerline of an intended track over an estimated reporting point. Over water, a tolerance of ±5 minutes from the estimated time over a reporting point or point of penetration and within 20 NM from centerline of an intended track over an estimated reporting point.

F. Airspace Classification Summary

The following section summarizes the requirements for operations within the various airspace classes.

1. Discuss "Class A" airspace.

Vertical dimensions: .... 18,000 ft MSL up to and include FL600
Operations permitted: .... IFR
Entry prerequisites: .... ATC Clearance
Minimum pilot qualifications: .... Instrument rating
Two-way radio communications: .... Yes
VFR minimum visibility: .... N/A
VFR minimum distance from clouds: .... N/A
Aircraft separation: .... All
Conflict resolution: .... N/A
Traffic advisories: .... N/A
Safety advisories: .... Yes

2. Discuss "Class B" airspace.

Vertical dimensions: .... Surface to 10,000 ft MSL
Operations permitted: .... IFR and VFR
Entry prerequisites: .... ATC clearance
Minimum pilot qualifications: .... Private/Student
Two-way radio communications: .... Yes
VFR Minimum visibility: .... 3 statute miles

Continued

VFR Minimum distance from clouds: .... Clear of clouds
Aircraft separation: .... All
Conflict resolution: .... Yes
Traffic advisories: .... Yes
Safety advisories: .... Yes

3. Discuss "Class C" airspace.

Vertical dimensions: .... Surface to 4,000 ft AGL (charted MSL)
Operations permitted: ....IFR and VFR
Entry prerequisites: ... ATC clearance for IFR; radio contact for all
Minimum pilot qualifications: .... Student certificate
Two-way radio communications: .... Yes
VFR Minimum visibility: .... 3 statute miles
VFR Minimum distance from clouds: ..... 500' below, 1,000' above,
and 2,000' horizontal
Aircraft separation: .... IFR, SVFR and runway operations
Conflict resolution: .... Between IFR and VFR operations
Traffic advisories: .... Yes
Safety advisories: .... Yes

4. Discuss "Class D" airspace.

Vertical dimensions: .... Surface to 2,500 ft AGL (charted MSL)
Operations permitted: ....IFR and VFR
Entry prerequisites: ... ATC clearance for IFR; radio contact for all
Minimum pilot qualifications: .... Student certificate
Two-way radio communications: .... Yes
VFR Minimum visibility: .... 3 statute miles
VFR Minimum distance from clouds: ..... 500' below, 1,000' above,
and 2,000' horizontal
Aircraft separation: .... IFR, SVFR and runway operations
Conflict resolution: .... No
Traffic advisories: .... Workload permitting
Safety advisories: .... Yes

5. Discuss "Class E" airspace.

Vertical dimensions: Except for 18,000 feet MSL, no defined
vertical limit. Extends upward from either the surface or a designated altitude to the overlying or adjacent controlled airspace.

Operations permitted: .... IFR and VFR
Entry prerequisites: .... ATC clearance for IFR
Minimum pilot qualifications: .... Student certificate
Two-way radio communications: .... Yes for IFR
VFR minimum visibility: .... *3 statute miles
VFR minimum distance from clouds: .... *500' below,
1,000' above, and 2,000' horizontal
Aircraft separation: .... IFR and SVFR
Conflict resolution: .... No
Traffic advisories: .... Workload permitting
Safety advisories: .... Yes

*Different visibility minima and distance cloud requirements exist
for operations above 10,000 feet MSL and Special VFR.*

6. Discuss "Class G" airspace.

Vertical dimensions: .... Surface up to but not including the
overlying controlled airspace or 14,500 MSL,
where Class E airspace begins, whichever occurs first
Operations permitted: .... IFR and VFR
Entry prerequisites: .... None
Minimum pilot qualifications: .... Student certificate
Two-way radio communications: .... No
VFR minimum visibility: .... *1 statute mile
VFR minimum distance from clouds: ... *500' below, 1,000' above,
and 2,000' horizontal
Aircraft separation: .... None
Conflict resolution: .... No
Traffic advisories: .... Workload permitting
Safety advisories: .... Yes

*Different visibility minima and distance from cloud requirements
exist for night operations, operations above 10,000 feet MSL, and
operations below 1,200 feet AGL.*

G. National Transportation Safety Board

1. When is immediate notification to the NTSB required? (NTSB Part 830)

The operator of an aircraft shall immediately, and by the most expeditious means available, notify the nearest NTSB field office when an aircraft accident or any of the following listed incidents occur:

a. Flight control system malfunction

b. Crewmember unable to perform normal duties

c. Turbine engine failure of structural components

d. In-flight fire

e. Aircraft collision in-flight

f. Property damage, other than aircraft, estimated to exceed $25,000

g. Overdue aircraft (believed to be in accident)

2. Define "aircraft incident." (NTSB Part 830.2)

An aircraft incident means an occurrence other than an accident associated with the operation of an aircraft, which affects or could affect the safety of operations.

3. Define "aircraft accident." (NTSB Part 830.2)

An aircraft accident means an occurrence associated with the operation of an aircraft which takes place between the time any person boards the aircraft with the intention of flight and all such persons have disembarked, and in which any person suffers death or serious injury, or in which the aircraft receives substantial damage.

4. Define the term "serious injury." (NTSB Part 830.2)

Serious injury means any injury that:

a. Requires hospitalization for more than 48 hours, commencing within 7 days from the date the injury was received;

b. Results in a fracture of any bone (except simple fractures of fingers, toes or nose);

c. Causes severe hemorrhages, nerve, muscle or tendon damage;

d. Involves any internal organ; or

e. Involves second- or third-degree burns affecting more than 5% of the body surface.

5. Define the term "substantial damage." (NTSB Part 830.2)

"Substantial damage" means damage or failure which adversely affects the structural strength, performance or flight characteristics of the aircraft and which would normally require major repair or replacement of the affected component. Engine failure or damage limited to an engine if only one engine fails or is damaged, bent fairings or cowling, dented skin, small punctured holes in the skin or fabric, ground damage to rotor or propeller blades, and damage to landing gear, wheels, tires, flaps, engine accessories, brakes, or wing tips are not considered substantial damage for the purpose of this part.

6. Will notification to the NTSB always be necessary in any aircraft "accident" even if there were no injuries? (NTSB Part 830)

Refer to the definition of "Accident." An aircraft accident can involve substantial damage and/or injuries, and the NTSB always requires a report if this is the case.

7. Where are accident or incident reports filed? (NTSB Part 830)

The operator of an aircraft shall file any report with the field office of the Board nearest the accident or incident. The National Transportation Safety Board field offices are listed in the U.S. government pages of telephone directories in major cities.

8. After an accident or incident has occurred, how soon must a report be filed with the NTSB? (NTSB Part 830)

The operator shall file a report on NTSB Form 6120.1 or 6120.2, available from NTSB field offices or from the NTSB, Washington D.C., 20594:

a. Within 10 days after an accident;

b. When, after 7 days, an overdue aircraft is still missing.

Note: A report on an "Incident" for which notification is required as described shall be filed only as requested by an authorized representative of the NTSB.

9. Can the FAA use reports submitted to NASA for enforcement purposes? (14 CFR 91.25)

No, the FAA will not use reports submitted to NASA under the Aviation Safety Reporting System for enforcement purposes. This system is a safety research program which uses pilot input in order to better understand and prevent hazardous situations that pilots encounter. By submitting a report within 10 days following a possible incident, a pilot is protecting himself from having a violation filed against him.

H. Aeronautical Information Manual

1. What type of aeronautical lighting is "VASI"? (AIM 2-1-2)

Visual Approach Slope Indicator (VASI) is a system of lights so arranged to provide visual descent guidance information during the approach to a runway. The basic principle of VASI is that of color differential between red and white: each light projects a beam of light having a white segment in the upper half and a red segment in the lower part of the beam. The lights in a two-bar VASI will be as follows:

Red Over Red—below Glide Path
Red Over White—on Glide Path
White Over White—above Glide Path

2. What is "PAPI"? (AIM 2-1-2)

The Precision Approach Path Indicator (PAPI) uses light units similar to the VASI, but are installed in a single row of either two- or four-light units. These systems have an effective visual range of about 5 miles during the day and up to 20 miles at night. The row of light units are normally installed on the left side of the runway.

Four white lights .... High (More than 3.5 degrees)
Three white one red .... Slightly high (3.2 degrees)
Two white two red .... On glide path (3 degrees)
One white three red .... Slightly low (2.8 degrees)
Four red lights .... Low (Less than 2.5 degrees)

3. What does the operation of an airport rotating beacon during the hours of daylight indicate? (AIM 2-1-8)

In Class B, Class C, Class D, and Class E surface areas, operation of the airport beacon during the hours of daylight often indicates that the ground visibility is less than 3 miles and/or the ceiling is less than 1,000 feet. ATC clearance in accordance with 14 CFR Part 91 is required for landing, takeoff and flight in the traffic pattern. Pilots should not rely solely on the operation of the airport beacon to indicate if weather conditions are IFR or VFR. There is no regulatory requirement for daylight operation and it is the pilot's responsibility to comply with proper preflight planning as required by 14 CFR Part 91.

4. What color are runway markings? Taxiway markings? (AIM 2-3-2)

Markings for runways are white. Markings for taxiways, areas not intended for use by aircraft (closed and hazardous areas), and holding positions (even if they are on a runway) are yellow.

5. What airport marking aids will be used to indicate the following? (AIM 2-3-2 through 2-3-6)

Runway Threshold Markings — These come in two configurations. They either consist of eight longitudinal stripes of uniform

Continued

dimensions disposed symmetrically about the runway centerline, or the number of stripes is related to the runway width. A threshold marking helps identify the beginning of the runway available for landing.

Displaced Threshold — A threshold located at a point on the runway other than the designated beginning of the runway. A displaced threshold reduces the length of runway available for landings. The portion of runway behind a displaced threshold is available for takeoffs in either direction. A ten-foot wide white threshold bar is located across the width of the runway at the displaced threshold. White arrows are located along the centerline in the area between the beginning of the runway and displaced threshold. White arrowheads are located across the width of the runway just prior to the threshold bar.

Runway Hold Position Markings —For taxiways, these markings indicate where an aircraft is supposed to stop when it does not have clearance to proceed onto the runway. They are also installed on runways only if the runway is normally used by air traffic control for "land, hold short" operations. They consist of four yellow lines, two solid and two dashed, spaced six inches apart and extending across the width of the taxiway or runway.

Temporarily closed runways and taxiways   Provides a visual indication to pilots that a runway is temporarily closed. Yellow crosses are placed on the runway only at each end of the runway.

Permanently closed runways and taxiways — For runway and taxiways which are permanently closed, the lighting circuits will be disconnected. The runway threshold, runway designation, and touchdown markings are obliterated and yellow crosses are placed at each end of the runway and at 1,000-foot intervals.

6. **What are the different ways a pilot might determine the proper runway and traffic pattern in use at an uncontrolled airport?** (AIM 4-3-3)

   a. At an airport with a full- or part-time FSS or a full- or part-time UNICOM in operation, an advisory may be obtained which will usually include wind direction, active runway, right or left traffic pattern, etc.

b. At those airports where these services are part-time or are not available, a segmented circle visual indicator system, if installed, is designed to provide traffic pattern information. It will consist of:

   i. the segmented circle;

   ii. the wind direction indicator — a wind sock, wind cone or wind tee;

   iii. the landing direction indicator — a tetrahedron may be used to indicate direction of landings and takeoffs (it is not accurate when winds are light);

   iv. landing strip indicators;

   v. traffic pattern indicators.

7. What is the standard direction of turns when approaching an uncontrolled airport for landing? (AIM 4-3-3)

When approaching for landing, all turns must be made to the left unless a traffic pattern indicator indicates that turns should be made to the right.

8. What is considered standard for traffic pattern altitude? (AIM 4-3-4)

Unless otherwise established, 1,000 feet AGL is the recommended traffic pattern altitude. At most airports and military air bases, traffic pattern altitudes for propeller-driven aircraft generally extend from 600 feet to as high as 1,500 feet AGL. Also, traffic pattern altitudes for military turbojet aircraft sometimes extend up to 2,500 feet AGL.

9. What recommended entry and departure procedures should be used at airports without an operating control tower? (AIM 4-3-3)

A pilot should plan to enter the traffic pattern in level flight, abeam the midpoint of the runway at pattern altitude. When departing a traffic pattern, continue straight out, or exit with a 45-degree turn

Continued

(to the left when in a left-hand traffic pattern; to the right when in a right-hand traffic pattern) beyond the departure end of the runway, after reaching pattern altitude.

10. If in doubt about the traffic pattern altitude for a particular airport, what publication can provide this information?

The Airport/Facility Directory.

11. What is an "ARTCC" and what useful service can it provide to VFR flights? (AIM Glossary)

An "Air Route Traffic Control Center" is a facility established to provide air traffic control service primarily to aircraft operating on IFR flight plans within controlled airspace and principally during the en route phase of flight. Air Route Surveillance Radar allows them the capability to detect and display an aircraft's position while en route between terminal areas. When equipment capabilities and controller workload permit, certain advisory/assistance service may be provided to VFR aircraft (VFR Flight Following). Frequencies may be obtained from the local FSS or the Airport/Facility Directory.

12. What are the following transponder codes? (AIM 4-1-19)

1200 — VFR operations
7500 — Hijack
7600 — Communications failure
7700 — Emergency

13. When conducting flight operations into an airport with an operating control tower, when should initial contact be established? (AIM 4-3-2)

When operating at an airport where traffic control is being exercised by a control tower, pilots are required to maintain two-way radio contact with the tower while operating within Class B, Class C, and Class D surface areas, unless the tower authorizes otherwise. Initial call-up should be made about 15 miles from the airport. Also, not all airports with an operating control tower will have Class D airspace. These airports do not have weather reporting, which is a requirement for surface-based controlled airspace. Pilots are expected to use good operating practices and communicate with the control tower.

14. When departing Class D airspace (airport traffic area), what communication procedures are recommended? (AIM 4-3-2)

Unless there is good reason to leave the tower frequency before exiting the Class B, Class C and Class D surface areas, it is good operating practice to remain on the tower frequency for the purpose of receiving traffic information. In the interest of reducing tower frequency congestion, pilots are reminded that it is not necessary to request permission to leave the tower frequency once outside of Class B, Class C, and Class D surface areas.

15. How do you convert from standard time to coordinated universal time? (AIM 4-2-12)

You should take the local time (converted to military time) and add the time differential to convert to UTC.

Eastern Standard Time: add 5 hours.

Central Standard Time: add 6 hours.

Mountain Standard Time: add 7 hours.

Pacific Standard Time: add 8 hours.

Alaska Standard Time: add 9 hours.

Hawaii Standard Time: add 10 hours.

Note: For Daylight Savings Time subtract 1 hour from above.

16. **Arrange the radio facilities listed below in the order they would be used when operating into or out of a tower controlled airport within Class B, C, or D airspace.**

    Approach Control
    ATIS
    Ground Control
    Control Tower
    Clearance Delivery
    Departure Control

    Arriving Aircraft: ATIS, Approach Control, Control Tower, Ground Control

    Departing Aircraft: ATIS, Clearance Delivery (if required for the surrounding airspace, i.e., Class B, C or D airspace), Ground Control, Control Tower, Departure Control.

17. **If instructed by ground control to "taxi to" the active runway, can you taxi across a runway if necessary?** (AIM 4-3-18)

    When ATC clears an aircraft to "taxi to" an assigned takeoff runway, the absence of holding instructions authorizes the aircraft to "cross" all runways and taxiways which the taxi route intersects except the assigned takeoff runway.

18. **What are "NOTAMs"?** (AIM 5-1-3)

    Notices To Airmen (NOTAM) — time-critical aeronautical information of either a temporary nature, or not known sufficiently in advance to permit publication on aeronautical charts or in other operational publications, receives immediate dissemination via the National NOTAM System. This is aeronautical information that could affect a pilot's decision to make a flight. It includes such information as airport or primary runway closures, changes in the status of navigational aids, ILS's, radar service availability, and other information essential to planned en route, terminal, or landing operations.

19. What are the three categories of NOTAMs? (AIM 5-1-3)

There are three types of NOTAMs generated by the FAA:

a. NOTAM (D) — A NOTAM given (in addition to local dissemination) distant dissemination beyond the area of responsibility of the Flight Service Station. These NOTAMs will be stored and available until canceled. NOTAM Ds contain information on all civil public use airports and navigational facilities that are part of the National Airspace System. NOTAM D items are serious enough to affect whether or not an airport or a certain facility is usable.

b. NOTAM (L) — A NOTAM given local dissemination by voice and other means to satisfy local user requirements. NOTAM L information may include conditions such as taxiway closures, persons and/or equipment near or crossing runways, airport rotating beacon outages and other information that would have little impact on non-local operations.

c. FDC NOTAM — The National Flight Data Center will issue these NOTAMS when it becomes necessary to disseminate information which is regulatory in nature. FDC NOTAMs contain such things as amendments to published IAPs and other current aeronautical charts. They are also used to advertise temporary flight restrictions caused by such things as natural disasters or large scale public events that may generate congestion of air traffic over a site.

20. What particular types of NOTAMs will be omitted in a pilot briefing if not specifically requested by the pilot? (AIM 7-1-3)

NOTAM (D) information and FDC NOTAMs which have been published in the Notices to Airmen Publication are not included in pilot briefings unless a review of this publication is specifically requested by the pilot. For complete flight information pilots should review the printed NOTAMs and the Airport/Facility Directory, in addition to obtaining a briefing.

21. Where can NOTAM information be obtained?
(AIM 5-1-3)

a. Nearest FSS

b. Airport/Facility Directory

c. Locally broadcast ATIS

d. Hourly surface observations

e. Notice to Airmen Publication (NTAP) — printed NOTAMs, not normally provided in a briefing; must make specific request for.

22. When are VFR flight plans required to be filed?
(AIM 5-1-4)

Except for operations in or penetrating a Coastal or Domestic ADIZ or DEWIZ, a flight plan is not required for VFR flight; however, it is strongly recommended that one be filed with an FAA FSS when making extended cross-county flights. This will ensure that you receive VFR Search and Rescue Protection.

23. What is a DVFR flight plan? (AIM 5-6-1)

Defense VFR; VFR flights into a Coastal or Domestic ADIZ/DEWIZ are required to file VFR flight plans for security purposes. The flight plan must be filed before departure.

24. When you land at an airport with an ATC tower in operation will the tower automatically close your flight plan?
(AIM 5-1-12)

Control towers do not automatically close VFR or DVFR flight plans since they do not know if a particular VFR aircraft is on a flight plan. A pilot is responsible for ensuring that his/her VFR or DVFR flight plan is canceled. You should close your flight plan with the nearest FSS, or if one is not available, you may request any ATC facility to relay your cancellation.

25. If your flight is behind schedule, and you do not report the delay, or you forget to close your flight plan, how much time from ETA does the FSS allow before search and rescue efforts are begun? (AIM 5-1-12)

If you fail to report or cancel your flight plan within one-half hour after your ETA, Search and Rescue procedures are started.

26. What is wake turbulence? (AIM Glossary)

A phenomena resulting from the passage of an aircraft through the atmosphere. The term includes vortices, thrust stream turbulence, jet blast, jet wash, propeller wash, and rotor wash, both on the ground and in the air.

27. Where are wake turbulence and wingtip vortices likely to occur? (AIM 7-3-3)

All aircraft generate turbulence and associated wingtip vortices. In general, avoid the area behind and below the generating aircraft, especially at low altitudes. Also of concern is the weight, speed, and shape of the wing of the generating aircraft. The greatest vortex strength occurs when the generating aircraft is HEAVY, CLEAN and SLOW.

28. What operational procedures should be followed when wake vortices are suspected to exist? (AIM 7-3-6)

a. *Landing behind a larger aircraft on the same runway:* Stay at or above the larger aircraft's final approach flight path. Note its touchdown point and land beyond it.

b. *Landing behind a larger aircraft, when parallel runway is closer than 2,500 feet:* Consider possible drift to your runway. Stay at or above the larger aircraft's final approach flight path, and note its touchdown point.

c. *Landing behind a larger aircraft - crossing runway:* Cross above the larger aircraft's flight path.

Continued

d. *Landing behind a departing larger aircraft on the same runway:* Note the larger aircraft's rotation point, and land well prior to rotation point.

e. *Landing behind a departing larger aircraft, crossing runway:* Note the larger aircraft's rotation point. If past the intersection, continue the approach, and land prior to the intersection. If larger aircraft rotates prior to the intersection, avoid flight below the larger aircraft's flightpath. Abandon the approach unless a landing is ensured well before reaching the intersection.

f. *Departing behind a large aircraft:* Note the larger aircraft's rotation point and rotate prior to the larger aircraft's rotation point. Continue climbing above the larger aircraft's climb path until turning clear of the larger aircraft's wake. Avoid subsequent headings that will cross below and behind a larger aircraft.

g. *Intersection takeoffs, same runway:* Be alert to adjacent larger aircraft operations, especially of your runway. If intersection takeoff clearance is received, avoid subsequent heading which will cross below a larger aircraft's path.

h. *Departing or landing after a larger aircraft executing a low approach, missed approach or touch-and-go landing:* Vortices settle and move laterally near the ground. Because of this, the vortex hazard may exist along the runway and in your flight path after a larger aircraft has executed a low approach, missed approach or a touch-and-go landing, particularly in light quartering wind conditions. You should ensure that an interval of at least 2 minutes has elapsed before your takeoff or landing.

i. *En route VFR (thousand-foot altitude plus 500 feet):* Avoid flight below and behind a large aircraft's path. If a larger aircraft is observed above or on the same track (meeting or overtaking) adjust your position laterally, preferably upwind.

29. What are several examples of illusions that may lead to landing errors? (AIM 8-1-5)

Runway width illusion — A narrower-than-usual runway can create the illusion that the aircraft is at a higher altitude than it actually is. The pilot who does not recognize this illusion will fly a lower approach, with the risk of striking objects along the approach path or landing short. A wider-than-usual runway can have the opposite effect, with the risk of leveling out high and landing hard or overshooting the runway.

Runway and terrain slopes illusion — An upsloping runway, upsloping terrain, or both, can create the illusion that the aircraft is at a higher altitude than it actually is. The pilot who does not recognize this illusion will fly a lower approach. A downsloping runway, downsloping approach terrain, or both, can have the opposite effect.

Featureless terrain illusion — An absence of ground features, as when landing over water, darkened areas, and terrain made featureless by snow, can create the illusion that the aircraft is at a higher altitude than it actually is. The pilot who does not recognize this illusion will fly a lower approach.

Atmospheric illusions — Rain on the windscreen can create the illusion of greater height, and atmospheric haze can create the illusion of being at a greater distance from the runway. The pilot who does not recognize these illusions will fly a lower approach.

Night
Operations

6

A. Night Preparation

1. Name the two distinct types of light-sensitive cells located in the retina of the eye. (AC 61-23C)

Rods and cones are the light-sensitive cells located in the retina.

2. What is the function of the cones, and where are they located in the eye? (AC 61-23C)

The cones are used to detect color, detail and far-away objects and are located in the center of the retina at the back of the eye. They are less sensitive to light, require higher levels of intensity to become active, and are most useful in the daylight hours.

3. What is the function of the rods, and where are they located in the eye? (AC 61-23C)

The rods are used for peripheral vision and are located in a ring around the cones. Rods are highly sensitive and are activated by a minimum amount of light; thus they are better suited for night vision.

4. What is the average time it takes for the rods and cones to become adapted to darkness? (AC 61-21A)

The cones will take approximately 10-15 minutes to adjust to darkness. The rods will take approximately 30 minutes to adjust to darkness.

5. What should the pilot do to accommodate changing light conditions? (AC 61-21A)

The pilot should allow enough time for the eyes to become adapted to the low light levels, and then should avoid exposure to bright light which could cause temporary blindness.

6. **Give some examples of illusions related to lighting conditions.** (AIM 8-1-5)

   a. Runway lights that are bright will tend to appear closer than they really are.

   b. If the horizon cannot be seen or distinguished, ground lights can be mistaken for stars.

   c. Inadvertently banking an aircraft away from a light can cause the sensation that the aircraft is too high, when in fact the aircraft could be too low.

7. **When approaching a well-lit runway surrounded by a dark area with little or no features, what illusion should a pilot be alert for?** (AIM 8-1-5)

   Featureless terrain illusion; this creates the illusion the aircraft is at a higher altitude than it actually is. The pilot who does not recognize this will fly a lower approach, possibly landing short of the runway.

8. **What should the pilot do to maintain good eyesight?**

   The pilot should be aware that alcohol, medication, fatigue, colds and other physical impairments can affect eyesight.

9. **What can the pilot do to improve the effectiveness of vision at night?**

   a. If possible, allow 30 minutes for the eyes to adjust to the darkness.

   b. Adjust the cockpit lights for optimum night vision and avoid bright light.

   c. Do not look directly at an object, try to look off-center since this will be more visually perceptive.

   d. Be aware that depth perception is inhibited due to lack of visual cues; thus, attention to airspeed, altitude, sink rates and attitude indicators must be maintained.

   e. Maintain a safe altitude until airport lighting and the airport itself are identifiable and visible. Many pilots have mistaken lighted highways for airports.

10. What equipment should the pilot have for night flight operations? (AC 61-21A)

Pilots should carry two flashlights, a white one for inspecting the aircraft during preflight, and a red one for examining charts during flight. The red light will not affect night vision as it does not glare; however, be aware that items printed in red on aeronautical charts will be harder to read.

11. What other items should the pilot have onboard for night flights? (AC 61-21A)

Pilots should have appropriate navigational charts, including any charts adjacent to the intended route of flight on board for night flight. These charts should be mounted on a clipboard or mapboard to prevent being lost in the dark cockpit.

12. Explain the arrangement and interpretation of the position lights on an aircraft. (AC 61-21A)

A red light is located on the left wing tip, a green light is located on the right wing tip and a white light is located on the tail. If the pilot observes both a green and red light on another aircraft, then the other aircraft is generally approaching the pilot's position. If the pilot sees only a green light, then the other aircraft is moving left to right in relation to the pilot's position. If the pilot sees only a red light, then the aircraft is moving right to left in relation to the pilot's position.

13. Position lights are required to be on during what period of time? (14 CFR 91.209)

No person may, during the period from sunset to sunrise:

a. Operate an aircraft unless it has lighted position lights.

b. Operate an aircraft that is equipped with an anticollision light system, unless it has lighted anticollision lights. However, the anticollision lights need not be lighted when the pilot-in-command determines that, because of operating conditions, it would be in the interest of safety to turn the lights off.

14. When an aircraft is operated in, or in close proximity to, a night operations area, what is required of an aircraft? (14 CFR 91.209)

The aircraft must:

a. be clearly illuminated,

b. have position lights, or

c. be in an area which is marked by obstruction lights.

15. Are aircraft anticollision lights required to be on during night flight operations? (14 CFR 91.209)

Yes; however, the anticollision lights need not be lighted when the pilot-in-command determines that, because of operating conditions, it would be in the interest of safety to turn the lights off.

16. What are the different types of lights found on an airport and what do they represent? (AIM Chapter 2)

a. *Rotating airport beacons*—used to identify the location of an airport, these beacons flash one or two colors alternately at regular intervals. Airports, landmarks and points on federal airways flash 12 to 30 times a minute. Heliport beacons flash 30 to 60 times a minute. The following color combinations are available:

   i. lighted land airport—white and green or green

   ii. unlighted land airport—white

   iii. lighted water airport—white and yellow or yellow

   iv. lighted heliport—green, yellow, and white

   v. military airport—white (dual peaked) and green

   vi. navigational point or landmark—white and red

b. *Obstruction lights*—used to identify hazardous areas to navigation and are indicated by flashing red beacons. High-intensity flashing white lights are used to indicate height obstructions such as transmission lines and chimneys.

c. *Runway lighting systems*—used to define the lateral limits of the airport's runway.

i. Runway edge lights—consist of a parallel set of white lights, except on instrument runways amber replaces white on the last 2,000 feet or half the runway length, whichever is less, to form a caution zone for landing. They are classified according to their intensity of brightness:

High Intensity Runway Lights .... (HIRL)
Medium Intensity Runway Lights .... (MIRL)
Low Intensity Runway Lights .... (LIRL)

ii. Runway threshold lights—consist of green lights across the runway threshold.

iii. Runway end lights—consist of red lights across the runway end.

iv. Runway End Identifier Lights (REIL)—consist of a parallel set of synchronized flashing lights located on each side of the runway threshold providing identification of the approach end of the runway.

v. Taxiway lights—consist of blue lights which indicate the usable taxiway:

Taxiway edge lights .... Blue
Taxiway centerline lights .... Green

vi. Touchdown zone lights—consist of two rows of transverse light bars disposed symmetrically about the runway touchdown zone. The system starts 100 feet from the landing threshold and extends to 3,000 feet from the threshold, or the midpoint of the runway, whichever is lesser.

vii. Runway remaining lights—consist of in-runway centerline lighting in the final 3,000 feet as viewed from the takeoff or approach position. Alternate red and white lights are seen from the 3,000-foot points to the 1,000-foot points, and all red lights are seen for the last 1,000 feet of the runway. From the opposite direction, these are seen as white lights.

17. How does a pilot determine the status of a light system at a particular airport? (AC 61-21A)

The pilot needs to check the Airport/Facility Directory and any Notices to Airmen (NOTAMs) to find out about available lighting systems, light intensities and radio-controlled light system frequencies.

18. How does a pilot activate a radio-controlled runway light system while airborne? (AC 61-21A)

The pilot activates radio-controlled lights by keying the microphone on a specified frequency. The following sequence can be used for typical radio controlled lighting systems:

a. On initial arrival, key the microphone seven times to turn the lights on and achieve maximum brightness.

b. If the runway lights are already on upon arrival repeat the above sequence to ensure a full 15 minutes of lighting.

c. The intensity of the lights can be adjusted by keying the microphone five or three times within 5 seconds.

B. Night Flight

1. During preflight what things should be done to adequately prepare for the night flight? (AC 61-21A)

a. Study all weather reports and forecasts. Particular attention should be directed towards temperature/dew point spreads to detect the possibility of fog formation.

b. Calculate wind directions and speeds along the proposed route of flight to ensure accurate drift calculations, as night visual perception of drift is generally inaccurate.

c. Obtain applicable aeronautical charts for both the proposed route as well as adjacent charts, and mark lighted checkpoints clearly.

d. Review all radio navigational aids for correct frequencies and availability.

c. Check all personal equipment such as flashlights and portable transceivers for proper operation.

f. The aircraft should be thoroughly preflighted.

g. All aircraft position lights, as well as the landing light and rotating beacon, should be checked for proper operation.

h. Ground areas should be checked for obstructions that may not be readily visible from within the cockpit.

2. What are some guidelines to follow during the starting, taxiing, and run-up phases of a night flight? (AC 61-21A)

a. The pilot should exercise extra caution on "clearing" the propeller arc area. The use of lights prior to and after engine startup can also alert persons in the area to the presence of the active aircraft.

b. During taxiing, avoid unnecessary use of electrical equipment which would put an abnormal load on the electrical system, such as the landing light. Additionally, other pilots taxiing in the area can be blinded by your landing light or strobes, so avoid using them during taxiing.

c. Taxi slowly and follow any taxi lines.

3. What are some of the guidelines to follow during takeoff and departure phases of a night flight? (AC 61-21A)

a. During takeoff the pilot should:

  i. on the initial takeoff roll, use both the distant runway edge lights as well as the landing light area to keep the aircraft straight and parallel in the runway, and

  ii. upon liftoff, keep a positive climb by referencing the attitude indicator along with positive rate of climb on the vertical speed indicator.

b. During climbout:

  i. do not initiate any turns until reaching safe maneuvering altitude, and

  ii. turn the landing light off after climb.

4. What should the pilot do to provide proper orientation and navigation during a night flight? (AC 61-21A)

a. The pilot should be aware of other aircraft and their relative positions to the pilot's aircraft. Landing lights of other aircraft can easily be confused with stars and other ground lighting.

b. The pilot should scan all flight instruments often to verify visual perceptions in order to avoid problems that may develop into critical flight attitudes, such as descending spirals.

5. If an engine failure occurs at night, what procedures should be followed? (AC 61-21A)

If the engine fails at night, the same procedures apply for dealing with the situation in the daytime. Maintain positive control of the airplane—do not panic. A normal glide should be established and maintained and the airplane turned toward an airport or away from congested areas. A check should be made to determine the cause of the engine failure, such as position of the magnetos, fuel selectors, or primer. If unsuccessful in restart procedures, select 7700 on the transponder and 121.5 on your radio. Declare an emergency, stating WHO you are, WHERE you are, and WHAT your intentions are. In some cases, where radar is available (Approach Control, Center, etc.) you may obtain a quick vector to the nearest airport if within gliding distance. If you have done your homework, you planned your route of flight within gliding distance of lighted airports. If not, two possibilities exist for emergency landing areas:

Lighted areas—interstate highways, roads, parking lots, etc. Advantages include being able to see where and what you are landing on, and having a relatively improved surface to land upon. Disadvantages include all kinds of obstructions to deal with, such as wires, poles, traffic, etc.

Unlighted areas—dark areas with relatively few lights indicating an open area such as a field, lake, etc. Advantages include few or no obstructions to deal with. Disadvantages include not being able to see what you have selected to land on until illumination by your landing light, and the higher possibility that what you have selected is unimproved, rough terrain, etc. As nearly as possible, land into the wind, with flaps, at minimum approach speed.

Complete a pre-landing checklist, and immediately before touch-down, secure all systems (electrical, fuel) and open the doors.

Whatever your decision, maintain positive control of the aircraft all the way down. A controlled crash will always be more survivable than an uncontrolled crash.

6. **What procedures should be followed during the approach and landing phase of a night flight?** (AC 61-21A)

   a. The pilot should identify the airport and associated airport lighting and runway lighting.

   b. The aircraft should be flown towards the airport beacon until the runway lights are identified.

   c. A powered approach should be used because visual perception during a descent at night can be difficult.

   d. The landing light should be switched on upon entering the airport traffic area.

   e. The pilot should avoid the use of excessive speed on approach and landing.

Aeromedical
Factors

7

Flight Physiology

1. What is hypoxia? (AIM 8-1-2)

Hypoxia is a state of oxygen deficiency in the body sufficient to impair functions of the brain and other organs.

2. Where does hypoxia usually occur, and what symptoms should one expect? (AIM 8-1-2)

Although a deterioration in night vision occurs at a cabin pressure altitude as low as 5,000 feet, other significant effects of altitude hypoxia usually do not occur in the normal healthy pilot below 12,000 feet. From 12,000 feet to 15,000 feet of altitude, judgment, memory, alertness, coordination, and ability to make calculations are impaired, and headache, drowsiness, dizziness and either a sense of well-being or belligerence occur. Effects are worse above 15,000 feet.

3. What factors can make a pilot more susceptible to hypoxia? (AIM 8-1-2)

The altitude at which significant effects of hypoxia occur can be lowered by a number of factors. Carbon monoxide inhaled in smoking or from exhaust fumes, lowered hemoglobin (anemia), and certain medications can reduce the oxygen-carrying capacity of the blood. Small amounts of alcohol and low doses of certain drugs, such as antihistamines, tranquilizers, sedatives, and analgesics can, through their depressant action, render the brain much more susceptible to hypoxia. Extreme heat and cold, fever, and anxiety increase the body's demand for oxygen, and hence its susceptibility to hypoxia.

4. How can hypoxia be avoided? (AIM 8-1-2)

Hypoxia is prevented by heeding factors that reduce tolerance to altitude, by enriching the inspired air with oxygen from an appropriate oxygen system, and by maintaining a comfortable, safe cabin pressure altitude. For optimum protection, pilots are encouraged to use supplemental oxygen above 10,000 feet during the day, and above 5,000 feet at night.

5. What is hyperventilation? (AIM 8-1-3)

Hyperventilation, or an abnormal increase in the volume of air breathed in and out of the lungs, can occur subconsciously when a stressful situation is encountered in flight. This results in a significant decrease in the carbon dioxide content of the blood. Carbon dioxide is needed to automatically regulate the breathing process.

6. What symptoms can a pilot expect from hyperventilation? (AIM 8-1-3)

As hyperventilation "blows off" excessive carbon dioxide from the body, a pilot can experience symptoms of lightheadedness, suffocation, drowsiness, tingling in the extremities, and coolness, and react to them with even greater hyperventilation. Incapacitation can eventually result from uncoordination, disorientation, and painful muscle spasms. Finally, unconsciousness can occur.

7. How can a hyperventilating condition be reversed? (AIM 8-1-3)

The symptoms of hyperventilation subside within a few minutes after the rate and depth of breathing are consciously brought back to normal. The buildup of carbon dioxide in the body can be hastened by controlled breathing in and out of a paper bag held over the nose and mouth.

8. What is carbon monoxide poisoning? (AIM 8-1-4)

Carbon monoxide is a colorless, odorless and tasteless gas contained in exhaust fumes. When inhaled, even in minute quantities over a period of time, it can significantly reduce the ability of the blood to carry oxygen. Consequently, effects of hypoxia occur.

9. How does carbon monoxide poisoning occur, and what symptoms should a pilot be alert for? (AIM 8-1-4)

Most heaters in light aircraft work by air flowing over the manifold. The use of these heaters while exhaust fumes are escaping through manifold cracks and seals is responsible every year for several nonfatal and fatal aircraft accidents from carbon monoxide poisoning. A pilot who detects the odor of exhaust or experiences symptoms of headache, drowsiness, or dizziness while using the heater should suspect carbon monoxide poisoning.

10. What action should be taken if a pilot suspects carbon monoxide poisoning? (AIM 8-1-4)

A pilot who suspects this condition to exist should immediately shut off the heater and open all air vents. If symptoms are severe, or continue after landing, medical treatment should be sought.

11. What is the cause of motion sickness and what are its symptoms? (AC 61-21A)

Motion sickness is caused by continued stimulation of the tiny portion of the inner ear which controls the pilot's sense of balance. The symptoms are progressive. First, the desire for food is lost. Then saliva collects in the mouth and the person begins to perspire freely. Eventually, he or she becomes nauseated and disoriented. The head begins to ache, and there may be a tendency to vomit. If the air sickness becomes severe enough, the pilot may become completely incapacitated.

12. What action should be taken if a pilot or his passenger suffers from motion sickness? (AC 61-23C)

If suffering from airsickness while piloting an aircraft, open up the air vents, loosen the clothing, use supplemental oxygen, and keep the eyes on a point outside the airplane. Avoid unnecessary head movements. Terminate the flight and land as soon as possible.

13. What is "ear block"? (AIM 8-1-2)

As the aircraft cabin pressure decreases during ascent, the expanding air in the middle ear pushes the Eustachian tube open. The air then escapes down to the nasal passages and equalizes in pressure with the cabin pressure. But during descent, the pilot must periodically open the Eustachian tube to equalize pressure. Either an upper respiratory infection, such as a cold or sore throat, or a nasal allergic condition can produce enough congestion around the Eustachian tube to make equalization difficult. Consequently, the difference in pressure between the middle ear and aircraft cabin can build to a level that will hold the Eustachian tube closed, making equalization difficult if not impossible. An ear block produces severe pain and loss of hearing that can last from several hours to several days.

14. How is ear block normally prevented from occurring? (AIM 8-1-2)

Normally this can be accomplished by swallowing, yawning, tensing muscles in the throat or, if these do not work, by the combination of closing the mouth, pinching the nose closed and attempting to blow through the nostrils (Valsalva maneuver). It is also prevented by not flying with an upper respiratory infection or nasal allergic condition.

15. What regulations apply and what common sense should prevail concerning the use of alcohol? (14 CFR 91.17)

The regulations prohibit pilots from performing crewmember duties within 8 hours after drinking any alcoholic beverage, while under the influence of alcohol, or having .04 percent weight or more alcohol in the blood. Due to the slow destruction of alcohol in the bloodstream, a pilot may still be under influence, or over the .04 percent mark, 8 hours after drinking a moderate amount of alcohol. Therefore, an excellent rule is to allow at least 12 to 24 hours from "bottle to throttle," depending on the amount of alcoholic beverage consumed.

16. **What regulations apply and what common sense should prevail concerning the use of drugs and medication?** (AIM 8-1-1)

Pilot performance can be seriously degraded by both prescribed and over-the-counter medications, as well as by the medical conditions for which they are taken. The regulations prohibit pilots from performing crewmember duties while using any medication that affects the faculties in any way contrary to safety. The safest rule is not to fly as a crewmember while taking any medication, unless approved to do so by the FAA.

17. **Discuss the effects of nitrogen excesses during scuba diving upon a pilot or passenger in flight.** (AIM 8-1-2)

A pilot or passenger who intends to fly after scuba diving should allow the body sufficient time to rid itself of excess nitrogen absorbed during diving. If not, decompression sickness due to evolved gas can occur during exposure to low altitude and create a serious inflight emergency. The recommended waiting times before flight are as follows:

Flight altitudes up to 8,000 feet:

a. Wait at least 12 hours after diving which has not required a controlled ascent.

b. Wait at least 24 hours after diving which has required controlled ascent.

Flight altitudes above 8,000 feet:

a. Wait at least 24 hours after any scuba dive.

Note: The recommended altitudes are actual flight altitudes above mean sea level and not pressurized cabin altitudes. This takes into consideration the risk of decompression of the aircraft during flight.

Notes

Notes

Notes